A LONGHAUL
TO
SUCCESS

by

Mary Middleton

To Steve,

Hope you enjoy my
book, with best
wishes.

Mary Middleton.

"A Longhaul To Success" by Mary Middleton

First edition published 2021 © Mary Middleton

ISBN: 978-1-3999-0909-9

Design & Layout, Nic Cairns, 22:22 Creative Media
Printed by © Ingram Content Group, www.ingramspark.com.

ACKNOWLEDGEMENTS:

I WOULD LIKE TO TAKE THIS OPPORTUNITY OF THANKING MY LOVELY PARTNER WHO HAS BEEN VERY PATIENT DURING MY WRITING OF THIS BOOK, HANDLING THE LAYOUT DESIGN AND FORWARDING THE BOOK TO THE PUBLISHER. ALSO SETTING UP THE COMPUTER, DESPITE MY PROTESTATIONS, SO THAT I COULD COMPLETE THIS ON THE MACHINE RATHER THAN BY WRITING IT ALL BY HAND, FOR WHICH I AM GRATEFUL.

ALSO TO RICK BAKER FOR ALL HIS HELP, GUIDANCE AND SUPPORT IN BEING ABLE TO PUBLISH MY FIRST BOOK, TOGETHER WITH MY SISTER SALLY AND MY FRIEND JAN WHO ASSISTED IN READING THE FINAL DRAFT.

I CONSIDER MYSELF TO BE SO LUCKY TO HAVE SUCH A WONDERFUL FAMILY AND FRIENDS WHO LOVE AND SUPPORT ME AND TO OUR DARLING GRANDSON FINLEY FOR THE VERY SPECIAL COVER HE DREW ESPECIALLY FOR MY BOOK.

I LOVE YOU ALL.

This novel is not entirely a work of fiction there is a great deal of non-fiction and the readers will have to make-up their minds for themselves which part is which.

Since writing this book we have all heard of the very sad death of Sir David Amess and are delighted that Her Majesty the Queen has given the City title to Southend-on-Sea something, he had been campaigning for many years and families past and present will be delighted with.

CHAPTER 1

Once upon a time - isn't that how all good stories and dreams start, for children maybe, but it is whether I would be able to take the dreams and fulfill them through to adulthood.

I supposed it really all started on the 11th June in the 50's - not to give too much away - when I was very rudely introduced to my grandmother (my mother's mother, or so I thought but later on I was to find out this was not actually the case). Find out later in the book, now you will have to go on reading, I'm not silly!

Although at this stage I do not remember but I was hung upside down by my grandmother, who luckily was the local midwife, and slapped unceremonially on the bottom until I gave my first cry. It must have been quite a task as I weighed in at 9lbs 8ozs but was much smaller than my big brother Michael who was 10lbs 3ozs. Brought tears to my eyes just thinking about it when I was giving birth myself many years later, that my mother had gone through this four times and with no pain relief.

Not a popular arrival from my brother Michael's point of view and he was to make sure I knew he was bigger than me right from the start and that he was in charge.

All my family lived in Southend-on-sea so I was an Essex girl and proud of it. My parents, after much discussion as my father wanted to call me Cora-Anne after an Irish family member, decided to call me after Walt Disney's daughter, who just happened to be called Sharon. As I grew up I realised I would bear the brunt of people's amusement, why could I not have been called Elizabeth? Even at an early age, I either called my dolls Elizabeth or Scarlet, I loved those names and decided one of them would be my stage name when I grew up, or if I ever had a baby girl.

I was the apple of my father's eye and although money was very short, he worked as a draughtsman in London and his boss bought me the most beautiful navy blue silver cross coach built pram. Pity about the pink fluffy outfits I had to wear that were irritating and annoying mittens that I would strive to get off so that I could play with the water that had landed on the apron of the pram when it rained. This resulted in a slapped hand, one of many from my mother.

I loved the people passing by and did not like to lay down despite my mother trying to get me to sleep. Sleep, I would be too afraid I would miss something, much better in the summer when the hood of the pram was down, apart from the stupid canopy that interrupted my view. I would often see the person called 'grandma' riding around on her bike in her nurse's uniform and on the front sat a huge great black bag. Sometimes she was in a hurry and would call out "Can't stop No 49 is about to deliver." Never understood what this meant until later on but I knew if she was on her rounds and not in a hurry she would stop and very often there would be something nice for me.

Grandma would cycle everywhere, although she was a bit wobbly at times and had, in the bad weather, a few accidents. She would cycle down to where grandad had his allotment where he would be busy gardening away. He always had a thing in his mouth which let out smoke and steam and smelt funny - I later found it was a pipe which grandma was not keen on and was always trying to get him to stop using. She never succeeded.

Very often my mother would push me in my pram down to see grandad and he would appear from his shed with cups of tea from a thermos flask, which seemed to appear whenever he was on his allotment but I never seemed to get any. I used to have boiled water with something called 'Delrosa' but I am sure the liquid in the flask would have been more exciting. We would always come away with lots of fruit and veg and he would always make sure everyone around had much the same, as food was still very short.

Howards dairy in Southend used huge shire horses to pull the milk cart and we always knew the milk was coming when we heard the horses hooves. My father would sometimes go out in the road with a spade to pick up the horse manure for his precious dahlias and grandad was always very pleased to receive a bucket of this precious fertilizer. All I remember that the smell was pretty awful and even worse it was still steaming - yuk!

During the Winter the milk bottles would freeze on the doorstep and the cream would come through the top and there would be a couple of inches of cream sticking up, which the birds loved if it was left there too long, very hygienic, but no one seemed too bothered.

The bread was always delivered by a man carrying a huge wicker basket, the 'rag and bone' man used to also ride round on his horse driven cart crying out for people to give their old rags and best of all was the coalman who used to deliver the coal from his lorry to the coal bunker. We were told to count the bags and I remember how slightly scary the coalman looked as even his face was completely covered in coal dust.

It always seemed there was something going on in our road until it snowed and everything seemed to stop when the snow became very deep, as it seemed to happen every Winter. There were very few cars on the roads so nothing damaged the beautiful white thick snow and it was not safe to bring the horses out. Even the pipes would freeze up and it would be extremely difficult to get water, which did not please grandma, who seemed to need loads of water to be boiled up, I heard her complaining one day.

On very rare occasions, school was closed and although everyone walked to school, however, the pipes were frozen and there was no water - hurrah! We, on the other hand, would find a cardboard box, tie a piece of string around it and use the road as a ski slope, having hours of fun until the box became too wet and disintegrated.

Grandad owned the local butchers and I often saw him amongst the meat, always jolly and smiling, so it was a very sad day when we were told that he had died, when I was about four and Michael was thirteen. We missed him a great deal and I remember it made everyone cry, especially grandma. He had always been a very popular figure evidently during the war when rationing was in place, making sure everyone got their fair share and maybe a little extra where families had lots of children to feed. My mother had been a land girl in the war and she and my grandma kept the allotment going for some time as it was grandad's pride and joy.

When I went back years later I was horrified to see that the allotments had all gone of course and in their place stood a huge ugly building, the VAT Office. It was hard to imagine that many years ago I had sat in my pram watching my grandad digging up his potatoes.

I was a real chatterbox from a very early age, nothing had changed from that point of view, a real Shirley Temple, especially as my mother would insist on putting those annoying rags in my hair overnight and then brush the curls out in the morning. If I made a fuss I would feel the weight of the brush with a slap on the top of my head, I never wanted the dreaded curls anyway.

My mother seemed to be getting much bigger and it was more difficult for me to sit on her lap. Little did I realise when I was sent to my favourite aunt for a couple of days that my grandmother would be riding on her bicycle round to our house with her big black bag.

Grandma often came around to visit but just recently she had been riding around on her bike as usual but she kept carrying her black bag, was the secret in that bag? Imagine my horror when I returned home to find that I had a new baby sister 'Yuk'. Maybe that is what grandma had in her bag, I hope she didn't come with her bag too often.

Did my father realise how this had happened? Perhaps he did not know what grandma had in her bag until it was too late!! No wonder I didn't know the facts of life until I was 14, as no one ever discussed things like childbirth, let alone how babies were made. Most of this information was learned from other girls in the playground, or from behind the bike sheds, certainly not ever discussed at the school I went to. In fact, it was strictly forbidden to discuss anything sexual. Even my father was asked to leave the room when those sorts of things were discussed by my mother and grandmothers.

I was introduced to this very small thing in her carrycot called Barbara, who seemed to take up a lot of time either crying or eating, although luckily she did not seem to eat in the same way as me, so I did not have to share which was good and she seemed to be unable to drink from a cup!!

Barbara did, however, bring with her a dolls pram and a beautiful dolly - what would I call her, maybe I would call her Elizabeth as that was my favourite name, or maybe Scarlet. I decided on Scarlet and after many trips to the dolls hospital my lovely Scarlet fell apart and was replaced with Pat, whom I still have today. Not sure why I called her Pat but her mama does not work when you tip her up and her hair is very wiry, everyone thinks she looks like something out of a horror movie as her eyes roll back.

Perhaps the baby would not be too bad, at least this time I could be the boss, or bigger sister as my mother kept telling me. Michael was 13 by now and I was never allowed to go in his room. I would have loved to get in his room and play with the glass balls that he kept in a tin but I was always told to 'get out'. I was 4 now and I was in charge and this new baby had better get the message.

My grandma on my father's side used to visit and she would always tell us stories of what it was like to be brought up in Ireland. Her parents were landowners and she was raised on a farm, which you would have thought idyllic but far from it, every night her father would get out the pony and trap and go down to the local where he would drink and gamble. He used to get so drunk the owners of the pub used to put him in the pony and trap and the pony always found its way home, as he had done it on so many occasions.

One day my grandma recollected her father waking up one morning to find that he had lost the farm, their home, on the throw of a dice but he had been so drunk he had no idea what he had done. They had no alternative but to leave the farm where she and her brothers and sisters had been born and raised and go and live in one of the smaller farms which was going to be quite a 'squash'. It was lucky that no one was occupying the farm at the time but as they overheard her mother shouting at her father saying they could have all been destitute because of his wanton ways but despite her threatening to leave him, his drinking and gambling continued until he died having lost most of the land the family owned.

She was the youngest of nine children but only seven actually survived. Her mother had gone to the door with the twins hanging around her skirt at the time and found a gypsy standing there selling pegs who told her "What beautiful children, pity they have only been loaned to you" which at the time she never understood but the twins died that following winter of Diptheria.

Grandma had never really liked school, as the pony and trap they went to school on was very rickety and her brothers were always being annoying, I could relate to that. It was thought that she was clever enough to become a teacher, which sounded horrific, however, she did become a teacher later on.

It was when she married grandad, my father's father, did they leave Ireland and move firstly to Suffolk and then to Essex where my father and his brother and sister were born. I would love to hear all her stories of being brought up on a farm and would listen to my two grandmas when they got together around the fire for a cup of tea, trying to outdo each other with their stories, in the nicest possible way.

CHAPTER 2

With the arrival of the new baby and my father doing well in his job, we moved and bought a house around the corner from the flat where I was born. One day I was awoken by a lot of commotion going on downstairs and when I reached the top of the stairs, I saw my father lying on the floor. I had never seen him like this and became very frightened as he was usually at work by now and why was he so still and quiet.

The doctor, who was a friend of the family, as did happen in those days, was sent for and I was ushered back to my bedroom by my mother. I could hear lots of talking, then my father being carried upstairs and into bed, where he stayed for the next three months. This seemed so strange to me as although I never saw my father during the week, he was always around during weekends and now I had been told by my mother that I had to play quietly and could only visit my father by standing at the bottom of his bed.

I remembered lots of comings and goings by different doctors and my grandmothers. I overheard different conversations saying if he did not start improving he would be taken away to a special hospital called Runwell. He had had a mental breakdown. Even as young as I was, it was strange to see my father who was a big 6ft tall man, always happy and laughing, hurrying off to catch the train to London to work, not able to even get out of bed. My mother had to feed him and the doctors were always in and out of the bedroom almost on a daily basis giving him instructions as to getting up, shaving, and going out for a walk.

In the early days, my father was unable to do any of the above and I overheard the doctors telling him if he had not done at least getting up and shaving by the end of the week they would have him admitted to Runwell. This sounded very scary to me and I was so glad, when at last, I could hear my father shuffling around the bedroom and gradually the door opened and he was standing at the top of the stairs. It took several days before he was able to go down the stairs and he looked very different now as he had grown a beard and looked like a pirate or someone who had been left on a desert island and just been found like Robinson Crusoe. At first, he used to walk as far as the front gate but was unable to go outside. Gradually he was able to open the gate and walk down the road.

As a child, I could not understand why this was a huge breakthrough but during his life, he suffered from his nerves and would need medication. It was not until I was much older did I realise how serious this must have been and why in many ways it changed his personality.

If it had happened nowadays, he would have received a completely different help and treatment.

It took 6 months until he was up and about and during this time I remembered he used to sit in a chair in the front room writing. He often wrote poetry but used to create bedtime stories for my sister and I. I was quite indignant when he created a mouse called Egbert Rumbletummy, who was chased by Michael the cat and Barbara the dog. Where was I in all these stories? One day I questioned my father, so he wrote a poem especially for my Sister and I:

'Sharon and Barbara little girls that I love sent to their daddy from heaven above and still there remains a place always there for the mother who bore this loveable pair'.

He wrote many pieces of poetry throughout his life and a couple of plays but I would always remember the above as it was like he was coming back into the world again from a very low dark place. I can honestly say I never ever heard my father swear and he never ever smacked us, despite being told by my mother "Just wait until your father gets home." His favourite saying was "not get or got" the verb is avoir, to have, and this has stuck with me, even today, when I use these words.

I was always in trouble with my mother and never saw time much after 6 o'clock, as I was always punished by having to ''go to bed at 6." If my mother gave a punishment, she never ever relented and my father would just say "try and be better tomorrow." It just never seemed to happen.

One day I heard a loud noise in the road and when we looked out of the window there was our father and he was getting out of a car. It was a grey Humber Hawk that he had bought and to everyone's excitment, we were told to jump in as we were going out for a drive in the country.

I could smell the leather seats and it was such fun to wind the windows down and watch people's faces as we drove by. There were very few people who had a car in our road and neighbours were very envious because we also had a telephone in our house as well and did not have to go to the corner of the road and stand outside a public telephone box until the person had finished their call, which seemed to take ages sometimes. Who would have imagined then that everyone would have a mobile phone in years to come!

My aunt decided to buy a hotel near the beach on the south coast and it was so exciting to jump in the car. My father would drive onto the ferry boat, either Mimi or Tessa, from the Essex side at Gravesend or Tilbury to the Kent side. Amazing to think that there is a tunnel and huge bridge now linking the two sides and how busy it is compared to waiting in a queue to board a ferry boat. Really, it was like changing one seaside town for another, and I was totally unaware at my young age I would return to this part of the world in later life.

CHAPTER 3

Just before I was 5, I started Kendrick which was a local school. My uniform was a cream shantung material dress with an orange K embroidered on the pocket, with a green and orange striped tie and green belt. The blazer was also bottle green with orange border and a green beret with orange pompom. White shoes and socks finished this ensemble off which woe betide if you got dirty. Obviously the headmistress must have had a thing about the colour orange.

I was always small and my mother always bought my clothes with 'plenty of room to grow', which frankly was laughable as I was the same size virtually throughout my early years, 4ft seemed to be the max, so the blazer came down past my dress, very fetching! Little did I realise, at this time, that there was worse to come on the uniform front.

Miss Hockley was my teacher and was very impressed that I could read already. She soon realised what a chatterbox I was and suggested that I have elocution lessons with Betty Bruckner. "Betty bought a bit of butter but she found the butter bitter so she bought a bit of butter to make Betty's bitter butter better." We had to say this out loud to start with then silently but making a popping sound with our lips every time the letter B came along. I was never quite sure what this did but we were told to practice this, as it would help us open our mouths using our facial muscles, like I needed that, and improve our diction.

I remembered Miss Bruckner had a mass of reddish coloured hair tied back with a chiffon scarf and looked as though she had just come off the stage. I absolutely loved her classes and she entered me for all the verse speaking exams at the festivals and I was lucky enough to play all the lead roles in any stage productions. I knew from an early age that I wanted to go on the stage when I grew up. I remember the excitement of being chosen to play the lead role of Alice, in Alice in Wonderland, when I was about 8. I had to learn all the lines for all four scenes and I will never forget my beautiful blue and white dress with blue alice band.

I used to always look out into the audience and hope that my Mother would be watching but she never came and it was a lesson I never forgot, as when I had my own children, I made sure that I went to everything they were in as I remember the disappointment I felt. I have seen other children go through this emotion looking for their parents who consistently never came to watch, whilst others would do everything they could to break their backs to get there in time to see a performance.

In fairness my Father, although he was working, used to try and get time off when he could and I was always thrilled to see him, especially if I was to receive a certificate or an award.

With the car, it enabled the family to go away on holiday, one year to the Isle of Wight and the next to Cornwall. The trunk with all our clothes had been picked up and gone ahead to arrive at the hotel before us. I remembered setting off very late at night in the hope that we would all remain asleep in the car to enable my father to drive in peace and quiet for most of the long journey.

The excitement of it all meant that I could not sleep and I kept fidgeting next to my brother, whilst my sister slept on the front seat with my mother. No seat belts or child seats in those days, in fact, I remembered my mother knitting whilst we drove along with my sister on the seat next to her. How things have changed.

My father took out membership of the AA and was very proud of his gleaming AA badge on the front of the car. There was much excitement as the AA man on his motorbike and sidecar drove by and saluted us and we would all wave back - bet they are glad this practice was abolished years ago!

I remember the days seemed to be a lot longer, the weather seemed to be much hotter and sunnier than nowadays and as a family we spent many happy days on the beach splashing around in the sea and building giant sandcastles. There was always a Punch and Judy show, which I am sure these days would be classed as far too violent but it was great fun, better than the television and donkey rides. My grandmother had a beach hut so we would go down to the beach in the summer and winter, taking our picnic and hotting up soup. It was on one of these days that the accident happened which would prove extremely challenging in later life.

Michael and I were swimming in the sea whilst my mother was nursing Barbara on her lap. "Climb on the lilo and I will pull you along," said Michael playfully. I was not able to swim and the water was getting quite deep when suddenly the water came over the lilo and I fell backwards.

I tried desperately to put one foot on the bottom but the water engulfed me and when I opened my eyes, all I could see was the colour of the red lilo above me. I remembered quite vividly, even to this day, gasping for air and thought I was going to drown. Michael suddenly realised that I was in great danger and as he was in charge he would be getting the biggest rollicking if something happened to me.

I felt Michael's hand as he hauled me out of the water, gasping and spluttering - he was so going to pay for this - his room would not be out of bounds much longer.

My mother arrived at this point and Michael got the biggest telling off - yes!! However, I never went into the sea again, only ever paddled and certainly would never ever swim. This would, in later life, prove extremely difficult to overcome as the deep-rooted fear of water was immense. My mother had medals for swimming and yet she never encouraged me to go back into the water and in those days there were no swimming classes at school, especially the school I would end up going to.

CHAPTER 4

When I was nine, my sister started at the same school. She was very bright and hated singing, dancing and acting, which was lucky for me as this was my chance to get out of looking after her. Whatever happened to my sister, I was always in trouble over it as I was not looking after her, or holding her hand.

I, on the other hand, never wanted to do school work and just wanted to act, dance and sing and was lucky enough to have voice training lessons with a Miss Austin, a soprano, who lived with her elderly mother in a big old scary house. She was very strict and I remembered sitting on a wooden hallstand waiting for my lessons and trying not to cough, as Miss Austin would call out 'stop coughing girl' as evidently it ruins the surface of your vocal chords!! So I would carefully open the front door, cough, and go and sit back on the hallstand, which was terrible if I had a cold but I loved these lessons, even the scales. Because Miss Austin took singing lessons at my school, I had been chosen for the choir.

My grandmother was getting much older now, and after several falls off her bike, had given up riding, so imagine my surprise when my mother announced she was expecting another baby. That black bag theory suddenly went completely out of the window.

My mother seemed to be putting on so much weight and she used to rest every afternoon and give us money to go to the local sweet shop and buy her a red or green Mivvi ice lolly, which was a great result as it meant we could have one too. My sister and I missed this treat when a few months later when I was 9, my brother Mark was born. My sister and I stayed at home this time and when we woke up there he was. Two to look after now I thought but at least two to boss around as well.

Even at this age, nine, I still remember the excitment of going to a friend's birthday party, dressed in our handmade party dresses and dreaded white socks and red shoes. If we were lucky, we would have special treats like crisps, chocolate biscuits and jelly and ice cream. We had such fun playing pin the tail on the donkey, musical chairs, musical bumps and best of all pass the parcel, where if we were extremely fortunate we would win the prize at the last wrapper. When it was time to go home everyone would receive a sweet. Can you imagine saying all of this to a nine year old now, they would just laugh. How things have moved on.

It was always explained to us that we were more fortunate than lots of other children, so when we collected all the Dr Barnardos little yellow and black houses from the different venues, shops, pubs etc.

they were piled up and the stopper on the bottom opened to release the money. We then counted all the pennies, threepenny bits and maybe some sixpences and the total was put on the back of the house with the new stopper put back and returned to the owners.

I absolutely loved doing this as we always had a talk and some slides about children in the care of Dr. Barnardos and they also produced Sunny Smiles that you could tear out the picture of the child and donate whatever money you could afford, usually an old penny.

I still have the little silver shield that was presented to me for taking part in this campaign and later on in life, I learned that one of my children's godparents had in fact been left in a carrier bag outside a telephone box, like many others at this time, and spent all of his life in a Dr. Barnardos home, as he sadly was never adopted.

By the time my youngest brother Mark was born, my elder brother Michael was 18 and was already working as a journalist for the Financial Times. He still lived at home and my father had bought an old Ford car from the elderly gentleman next door, who had given up driving, for Michael to use. That car had running boards down each side and the windscreen opened by using a handle on the dashboard. Michael would practice going up and down the driveway beside our house and one day he left the starting handle in the front of the car and it went straight through the end of the prefabricated garage.

The noise was horrendous and he was in so much trouble, which made a change as it was usually myself in trouble. When they went to the bottom of the garage, there was the starting handle poking out of the end of the garage and our mother was telling Michael to make himself scarce, whilst she explained to his father when he got home just how this had happened. Shortly after this, Michael passed his test and he and his girlfriend used to go out driving and if we were lucky they would take my sister and I out in the old car. We had to carry a watering can because the car seemed to constantly need topping up, as the radiator had a hole in it.

My sister and I actually loved looking after our baby brother, who was now two years old. One day I overheard my parents discussing going to a place in Kent, to look at buying a new house and moving somewhere in that area. How could they? I was 11 and desperately wanted to go to drama school and loved it where we lived as we were so near the beach we could go every day. Even worse was to come, when visiting our new house I had to go to visit my new school. As we drove down this long drive I had a terrible feeling about this.

There in front of me was this huge old creepy building and to my horror when my parents rang the huge clanking doorbell, who should be standing in front of me but Mother Superior. I had only ever seen nuns in films and I was not even a Catholic. How come I had to go to this awful place as this was a convent, not a school and I was definitely not going to stay there. I bet they would not even know anything about music, apart from the Sound of Music!

Mother Superior and Mother Martha, who was a real tyrant, welcomed me with 'And who do we have here' - like she was not expecting me and my visit was a complete surprise. I had this urge to say something cheeky but I held my tongue as the look from my parents said it all - I had to behave or else I would be in trouble.

I so wanted to be called Elizabeth even more desperately as now I was going to be an Essex girl, called Sharon and going to a convent school. How I was going to be laughed at but somehow I thought there was maybe very little laughter going on in this place. I would change my name to a stage name later on.

The uniform was horrible - I was very small still, only just about 4ft 10" so the long skirt and raincoat, which were well below my knees drowned me - I was told I would grow into them which I never did as I only reached 5ft 3" fully grown. To top it off a straw boater, white gloves and thick black tights, with brown brogue shoes, again very fetching and it made the Kendrick school uniform seem quite trendy!

The brown briefcase was so heavy, it was like carrying a suitcase, especially when it was loaded with books and as I was so small it virtually reached the ground. Thank goodness for the bag with all my precious dancing shoes, not that I supposed I would be doing much dancing in this place.

I was introduced to the other girls and at least they were friendly and once the nuns knew I could sing they insisted on me taking Latin classes to enable me to sing in the chapel and at weddings. This was supposed to be a privilege as usually only the Catholic girls were chosen. Some privilege as it was always on a Saturday which was like having to go to school at the weekend.

Without my best friend Sandra, who was catholic and had to take part in all the catechism and days of silence, which I knew I would have no chance of keeping, my school days would have been terrible, but if Joanne Lumley could do it, I sure would give it a try.

Full weddings were over 2 hours and myself and the other girls would be up on the balcony. I used to get bored and as Eric Morecambe would say 'I was singing the right words but not necessarily in the right order'. It made the other girls laugh and invariably, especially in the chapel, I would be severely reprimanded. Needless to say, I did not do well in my Latin exams but passed all my scripture exams!!

I knew I would be the laughing stock of all the children on the two buses I had to take to reach home. Luckily my best friend Sandra caught the first bus, which helped, as we tried to stuff our expensive boaters into our briefcases but the stupid boaters were fast losing their shape. At least in the winter, the boaters were replaced with a round felt hat that looked like divided cakes and were a lot easier to wear and stuff away. I vowed and declared no more uniforms for me once I was grown up.

The nuns did not approve of the stage but the carrot for me was if I did well in my exams my parents might allow me to go to stage school. There was very little drama at my school, apart from if you broke the rules, like running in the corridors which was strictly forbidden. Equally so was using the main wooden staircase that the nuns only were allowed to use and was polished to within an inch of its life every day or using profanities, ie. shut up or anything with any sexual connotations, how different things are today thank goodness.

These misdemeanours would result in a B for discipline. If a D was given, the result would be a detention at the end of the week which involved 100 lines stating "I must control the action of my vocal chords" especially if swearing had been involved. The lines would then be torn up right in front of you, all that effort and not even looked at.

What little acting there was, I always managed to get a part in and the dancing teacher, Miss Cameron, I loved. I took ballet and Scottish dancing classes and I loved the white dress with the tartan sash and black ballet shoes. Together with my pink pointe ballet shoes, I just lived for these classes and made my school days bearable. I never quite understood the need for Scottish dancing, after all when and where in the South of England was I ever going to do the Dashing White Sergeant or the Gay Gordons, but it would come in handy maybe on a visit to Scotland one day, or visiting royalty!

I learned how to cook, dressmake, lay formal tables for dinner parties and walk with a book on my head for good deportment as slouching was certainly never allowed. I learned how to get in and out of a car without exposing any underwear and not to cross my legs but tuck one foot behind the other when sitting down, no legs wide open would be tolerated on any account!

The nuns were extremely strict and if we passed by any of them without genuflecting (curtesying), we would be in serious trouble. I also wondered how I, or any of my class, ever learned the facts of life as these were never ever discussed neither at home or at school. However, there was one girl who had an older brother and sister and she filled us in on all the missing details! Risque questions would have resulted in a trip to Mother Superior's office. In fact when one day one of the girls suddenly went missing and her desk cleared, no one could understand where she went and why not even a goodbye. We were never allowed to even mention her name and it was not until later in life that I realised the girl was pregnant.

I remember my Aunt had a house in Tunbridge Wells and when we used to visit we were told not to go all the way to the bottom of the garden where there was a huge hedge. Of course my sister and I were curious, well at least I was so I dragged her along to see where the noise was coming from, as I could hear girls voices and the sound of babies crying. We were severely reprimanded by my Aunt as we were not allowed to talk to the girls in the Naughty Girls house, which was behind the hedge, gosh they must have been bad I remember thinking to put babies in there, how bad could a baby be.

I remember in the Winter the hedge was not so thick and I chanced the wrath of my Aunt and called out to some of the girls to talk to them, as I felt so very sad for them, even at my young age this did not seem right. It was some years later that I found out it was a home for Unmarried Mothers to have their babies and be put up for adoption, it all seemed so very cruel but my mother warned me I would end up in one of those homes if I ever came home pregnant. How life has changed, luckily for the better,

The same occurred whilst one of the teachers, who was not in the 'Order' was taking a literature class and reading a book "My Cousin Rachel' by Daphne du Maurier. She would be reading along when all of a sudden she would stop and become all discombobulated and say this part was not suitable for young ladies and would miss these sections out. It was not until later on when I was reading the book again for myself that I realised that anything that had a slight sexual connotations would not have been allowed and therefore not read out to us girls.

However, I always seemed to have the same wording on my reports 'Could do Better' and I suppose alot of adults look back on their school years and wish maybe they had done better, I know I do.

CHAPTER 5

Having miraculously passed most of my exams, even to the surprise of most of the nuns and teachers, my cousin who was working as an extra and had been a stand in for Richard Burton, arranged for me to have an audition in London for a musical. At last, I was on my way to stardom but my parents had arranged a nice secretarial course for me, 'something to fall back on' they said and if I passed all my secretarial exams they might consider stage school. 'Don't put your daughter on the stage Mrs Worthington' was continually thrown at me and I needed to get a 'proper job', so sadly it never happened. When I see Joanna Lumley and how well she has done, I wonder just what might have been if I had been allowed to follow in her footsteps.

So secretarial college it was, would I ever keep up with the shorthand. So many words and symbols and as the speed became quicker and quicker, it was so easy to lose my concentration, even for a minute, which would mean that I would not be able to read it back and then type it out correctly. I just hoped the person I worked for spoke very slowly and what I did not get down I could make it up without being noticed. The typing was alright but as for the book-keeping, even getting to trial balance was a mystery and I knew going into accountancy was not for me.

The highlight of my course was when I arrived home and found my parents discussing an invitation they had received from Buckingham Palace. My uncle played polo and my parents and I had been invited as part of their family, to attend the garden party at Windsor.

I was so excited, perhaps all those classes at the convent had not been in vain, although I do not remember the art of being able to curtsy, I had plenty of time to practice. I could not wait to go to college and tell everyone, I would have to be vetted and they would require a reference from the college that I had not been involved in any illegal activities or been on any 'Ban the Bomb' marches!!

What should I wear? It took ages to decide and hundreds of shops to visit with my friend Sandra to choose something that would be suitable for the occasion and agreeable to my parents. A proper hat this time and not one of those awful school berets and definitely not a boater, no white gloves but a pair of beautiful three-quarter length beige kid gloves.

I was so excited and even more so when the Queen and Prince Philip walked right in front of us. I could not believe how small the Queen actually was, even smaller than myself, her complexion was flawless and much prettier in real life. I was so overwhelmed I nearly forgot

Mary Middleton

the curtsy, I had been practising for weeks as the Queen passed by me with the rest of the royal party. It was an amazing occasion and one I would never forget.

Lots of my friends from college went to London to work in offices and I did just that. I remember how nervous I felt as I boarded the train at Tonbridge and arrived at Charing Cross as I did not know my way around London, certainly the underground was a complete mystery as were the buses. I had only been to London sightseeing with my parents and it was very daunting to think that I could be working there and travelling by train every day. I needed to work out how the underground worked, especially the circle line which I soon realised, if I was not careful, I could end up going the wrong way round.

As luck would have it, the No 6 or 15 bus would take me from outside Charing Cross Station to Regent Street which was where I went to work at Libertys in Regent Street as a secretary in the Advertising department. I first met the head of the Department, very scary and she liked everything to be just so. I don't think I would be making up anything that she dictated, it seemed she would be likely to remember every word. Luckily I was offered the job and I started travelling to London with great excitement, it was like a new adventure.

After a few days I went with my colleagues to visit the big fashion houses, who would choose items from the store and have them collected. Once photographed they would be listed in their magazines like Vogue, Cosmopolitan and Harpers Bazaar. Copies of the publications were sent to our Department whereupon I would have to cut the article out and paste it in a huge scrapbook. Either myself or one of my colleagues used to meet the advertising people from the different fashion houses, as it was not only good publicity for them but also for the store. Going round to Vogue, which was in Hanover Square just around the corner to Liberty's and seeing how it was all photographed was so exciting for someone like myself who was really only young and out of college.

The items taken from the store were literally anything from home and ware to very expensive fabrics and furs from Bonne Cashin, some of which were of huge value and had to be returned the same day. On one particular day the shoot over-ran and it was agreed they would be allowed to be returned in the morning. Unfortunately, the fashion house was broken into during the night and all the items on loan were taken. This was my first taste of real working life as it caused quite a stir, especially being the new girl on the block. I was really scared of being interviewed and even though I knew nothing about the missing garments, I am sure I had guilt written all over my face and the boss was in an indescribeably bad mood and everyone was afraid to speak to her.

Amid all the controversy with the loss of the above, I was required to attend the boardroom to take the minutes of meetings with the owner of the store Mr. Stewart Liberty. As this was the first time I had used my shorthand I was terrified of not being able to keep up and my boss was not in the right mood to ask her to repeat anything. I need not have worried, I soon realised why there were ramps all over the store, which I just thought were for ease of access for wheelchair customers, but when I arrived at the meeting I saw that Mr Liberty was in a wheelchair. He was like an old friendly grandad and immediately put me at my ease and told me to come and sit next to him. If I was not able to keep up or did not understand something, he would help me, much to my boss's annoyance. I was so young I must have looked like a frightened shrew but throughout my time at Liberty's, he was one of the nicest and kindest person I had ever known.

When I left work in the evenings at the back of the store, I saw Mr. Liberty being pushed in his wheelchair by his chauffeur, who drove a navy blue Humber Super Snipe. My father had a green one just the same and when I went to the next meeting I was able to chat with him about his favourite car. If he was in the store when I was taking notes with the fashion houses, he would always give me a wave and stop and chat if he was not too busy, I really liked him. As this was my first job, his help gave me the confidence I would need as working in London at such a young age and seeing all the models and photographers were very glamorous but I needed my wits about me.

We used to get paid on a Friday in cash in a small brown envelope with the deductions on the front. I was paid £16 a week, about £12 after deductions, which was a huge amount but out of this, I had to pay my train fare and give my mother £1 for my keep. The highlight of the week was on a Friday to meet up with two other girls from college and go to the Wimpy Bar just off Oxford Street and have hamburger, chips and a drink for about a £1 in old money. I remember I had to walk past the Palladium which always had billboards advertising Sunday Night at the London Palladium and very often I would hang around to see celebrities going in and out of the stage door.

CHAPTER 6

I was sixteen now when my friend from college asked if I would like to go on holiday with her and her family as they were going to the Isle of Man for her father's business combined with a holiday.

My parents agreed I could go and we all set off, firstly by train from Tunbridge-Wells to London, then London to Liverpool where we caught the ferry over to Douglas in the Isle of Man. It was extremely rough and I hoped when the boat stopped rocking the sickness would pass once we were on dry land.

My friend Janet and I were so excited as this was the first time I had ever been away from home without my parents on holiday. We shared a room in a beautiful hotel and set about unpacking our huge amount of clothes, many of which were handmade by themselves and so short just as to allow some movement without too much stretching.

Janet's parents took us out to a huge dance hall as her father was meeting his clients who were celebrities and judging the Miss Douglas Isle of Man Carnival Queen competition. Suddenly in front of me was Manfred Mann, Sounds Incorporated and Albert Tatlock whom I had only ever seen on the television on Coronation Street and here he was right in front of me.

A form was suddenly thrust in my hand and before I knew it I was asked to fill it in and was entering the Carnival Queen competition. I spent all next day deciding on what I would wear and how I would do my hair - Janet, unfortunately, was not able to apply as her father was involved with the promotion.

It was packed in the dance hall and suddenly I became nervous as I was asked to line up with the other girls. To my amazement, I was called forward by the judges and was on the list of finalists to be judged the next day. I was so excited and I felt like a star up on the stage even, if it was for a short time.

I was used to being on the stage but when I was called forward to speak to the judges, I was more nervous under the spotlight than I had ever felt. I could not even remember what I had replied but suddenly as I turned round to see where Janet was, I was aware of the compare calling out the names of the girls in third and second position, then of my name being called and the girl next to me flinging her arms around my neck. I had only gone and won. I was Miss Douglas Isle of Man 1967.

I was suddenly aware of a beautiful handmade sash being put over my head by a local DJ and Albert Tatlock presenting me with lots of wonderful prizes. The rest of the evening I was in a complete daze. The organisers explained what would be expected of me as I had duties to perform all week, culminating in being on a float which would be driven all along the seafront before arriving at the Villa Marina ballroom for evening entertainment.

The whole week was a blur as Carnival week is very special in the Isle of Man, starting with the crowning ceremony. I could not believe it, as I had no idea what to expect, when the next morning the organisers arrived at our hotel. The telephone in our room rang and I was asked if I was ready for the clothes that I would be wearing for the next week to be brought to my room, it was like being a film star.

About four different people arrived at my door with the most beautiful white lace wedding gown with a very full skirt with lots of taffeta petticoats, it hardly fitted through the doorway. I was actually going to be wearing this, I just hoped it fitted, but I was told that the dresser would make any alterations necessary. I hoped she had plenty of material for taking the dressing out and there was so little time as we were due to leave for the crowning ceremony in about an hour's time.

Good thing I was wearing all my best white underwear as I stepped into this wonderful dress and the dresser pulled all the material up over my hips and as I started to breath in, she started to pull the zip up. What a result as it actually fitted, much to the relief of everyone in the room as pins were stood down. When I turned and looked at myself in the mirror, I could not believe it was me! I looked like something out of a Disney princess film.

Next came the satin Carnival Queen sash I had received the night before and then came the tricky part, the red velvet cloak which was extremely long and heavy. This was put on and the tapes tied behind my back but I soon realised just why I would need the assistance of the six little carnival princesses that would be carrying the cloak, as once I started to walk the weight of the dress plus the cloak nearly pulled me backwards, and this was without the crown which was also quite heavy. Still if the Queen can do it, I certainly can.

I was given a quick run down of what was to happen throughout the next few days but I was really not fully prepared as to just how wonderful this experience was going to be, it was like living in a dream. There was suddenly a knock on the door and standing in the doorway was Jerry, blonde, good-looking, a local policeman who was introduced to me as my 'bodyguard/chaperone'. Just when I thought things could not get any better, I get a Kevin Costner lookalike and he is all mine. We were quickly introduced and then Jerry suggested we make a move as time was pressing, as he took my hand and started to guide me through the hallway. I was happy just to hang on to him, in fact for once I was lost for words, which does not happen often.

23

Trying to negotiate through the bedroom door and into the lift took some doing but as the lift doors opened, there were so many people waiting in the foyer, not just people staying at the hotel but people who had found out where I was staying and then there were members of the press. It was like I imagined it would be at the Oscars with cameras flashing whilst everyone was fussing round me trying to get the huge dress and cloak nicely arranged for the photos. Smiling and waving which at the end of the week was the most exhausting part, but for the moment I was just enjoying the experience. especially as I could see Jerry out of the corner of my eye.

Time to leave, I could see Jerry out the corner of my eye and he was moving forward to clear the way to escort me outside to his beautiful blue sports car where he would transport me to the crowning ceremony. My friend Janet and family were being taken in a car which would follow behind.

With the huge dress and red cloak, it was quite a squash to fit into a small 2 seater sports car but luckily I was to sit on the back so that everyone could see me and I could wave and hopefully not fall off. Jerry had a very naughty wicked smile as he asked if I was comfortable and did I always wear so many clothes. I suggested maybe he needed to buy a bigger car. He promised to drive slowly as cars would move out of our way and managed to drive me to the Winter Gardens whilst explaining to me what was about to happen.

My friend Janet was in charge of crowning the little princess and then helping me and my little attendants. As I prepared to make the walk through the gardens, I was suddenly aware of hundreds of people sitting in deckchairs awaiting my arrival. Jerry helped me out of the car, which believe me took some doing, I have never seen so much material but I suddenly felt really nervous. He must have sensed this as he squeezed my hand and told me I looked absolutely beautiful, I was ready to make my entrance.

The outgoing Carnival Queen for the previous year appeared and as she stood in front of me she whispered that the crown was quite heavy and to be prepared. She was right, the crown was really heavy and did not allow for much movement and having made my unrehearsed speech, which I was unaware I would have to make in front of the whole of the Winter Gardens full of people, the celebrations began.

During the downtime when I did not have any duties to perform, Janet and I went with Jerry and his friend and they took us over the TT track. As both of them were policemen, they had often been on duty marshalling the race. I know very little about motor bikes but I can see how skilful the riders would have to be as the terrain was extremely harzardous in parts, but I could see why it was so popular.

The people were so friendly and the week was full of judging, presenting prizes and culminated in me leading the carnival procession in a shell on a float that drove all along the promenade, to the end of week Carnival Ball. Sadly the Carnival Queen is not allowed to dance with her bodyguard but it would have been incredibly difficult to get near me. When I first started, I loved the idea of smiling and waving but after a week my arm and face were so tired, I definitely needed a massage!! With Jerry and Janet's help we managed to negotiate most places with all my regalia, especially with the addition of the crown which meant I could not move my head very easily. It was so much easier when Janet and I could sneak out of our hotel in our own clothes, especially getting in and out of Jerry's sports car. He would tease me 'less clothes I see tonight'.

When it was time to leave the island, I was extremely sad as we had had a wonderful holiday, never in my wildest dreams could I have ever imagained this happening to me and everyone had been so kind to us and made us so welcome. I had in just one week become very close to Jerry as everywhere I turned he was always there, smiling and reassuring and although maybe it was a holiday romance, I was delighted when he arrived at the quayside to say goodbye to us, hoping maybe he would miss me, as much as I would miss him. Luckily, he felt the same.

This was the start of a long-distance relationship for Jerry and I, in fact, my first real boyfriend. We spoke on the telephone once or twice a week when his shifts allowed and I still have all the letters he wrote to me, yes wrote, seems strange to say both of the above now. As I was working in London, I was able to leave work and go straight to Heathrow and fly out to the Isle of Man on a regular basis. It was very scary at first, I had never experienced going to an airport as I had never even been on a holiday abroad but it was so much quicker than taking the train and boat. It was on one of these trips that I suddenly realised how exciting this mode of travel was as I watched the air stewardesses moving around the aircraft. I remembered that my cousin was a BOAC stewardess and I would have to make contact with her to see whether my joining would be possible.

I soon learned that applicants had to be 21 years old, unmarried and of course no children. I would have to put this on the back burner and wait for some time before I could apply to the airlines to be considered for a job but it was definitely on my agenda when the time came.

Once Jerry came to visit me at home and to meet my parents but on the weekend he was staying we were hit by the 1968 floods.

We were living in a bungalow, when my younger brother gave the alarm. The water was already pouring down the driveway bringing the big oak gates with it and my parents suddenly realised that they could actually hear the torrent of water and he was not joking. The river that ran down the side of our house was a stream fed from the River Medway that had broken its banks and was now pouring into our house. With my father being a draughtsman, I recalled standing in the filthy water handing the drawings up the metal ladder into the loft. With the water getting deeper and so cold, we knew very little would be salvaged. The water was now rising fast and it seemed to be coming in everywhere, even up through the toilets which meant we were standing in this foul smelling water. I was getting scared as there was no escape but to swim and that just was not going to happen for either myself, nor my father, as we both were non swimmers.

We had no choice but to climb up the ladder into the loft and wait there until help arrived, which it did by way of a boat being rowed down the driveway. The whole family including Jerry were taken into the boat from the roof of the bungalow to the safety of a local hotel. The River Medway had burst its banks and we stood in the high street just watching as washing machines, tumble driers etc floated down the river only to be looted. Once the water had subsided, we were allowed back into the house and the devastation was terrible as everything was destroyed, apart from my father's drawings which luckily were high enough to escape the waters. We had to leave the house with only a few belongings that we managed to salvage for about six months.

The Salvation Army brought in heaters after the water had subsided but the foul smell was everywhere. Even effluent was stuck to the walls so I can fully appreciate how people feel when they live close to the water and keep being flooded. As the stream that ran down the side of our house emptied into the Medway, measures had to be taken so the land never flooded again. To the best of my knowledge this area has never flooded in this way since, but my mother never really got over it and wanted to move from that point on.

A year had passed by so quickly and I managed to go backwards and forwards to visit Jerry for the weekend when he was off duty and was especially exciting when he was marshalling the TT races. Watching the bikes go through all the little villages on the roads, which were really rough in places and the corners quite treacherous, was thrilling. Being part of this huge event and being with Jerry, who was a bit older than me, was a really special time in my young life.

I had to return to the Isle of Man to crown the new Carnival Queen the following summer but I knew the long-distance relationship was proving not only expensive but extremely difficult to maintain. I was not ready for a permanent move to the island away from family and friends, much as I had enjoyed the whole experience as it is a beautiful island and the people were really lovely. Jerry and I parted amicably short thereafter.

CHAPTER 7

My relationship with my mother had never been very good and life had become so difficult at home that I decided it would be better for me to leave home. I found a flat which I found incredibly hard to support as rent on the flat together with bills left me very little to live on, so I knew I would have to leave my London job to save on the train fares.

Before I left London I met my eldest brother Michael, who was now married with children and had lunch with him. He told me he had something to tell me that he thought I should know. He was only my half brother as my mother had been married before when she was very young; she had divorced his father whom he had never met. My grandmother had in fact brought Michael up and when our mother remarried, my father had adopted him and it was never discussed. He was sent away to boarding school when our parents married and I came along. Suddenly, it all fitted into place as I realised why Michael had disliked me so much, why on earth my parents had not told us was beyond me as it would have saved all the resentment. It was not until Michael and I were much older did we really discuss our childhood and I fully understood how he felt.

I am so glad that nowadays things are much more open and discussed more freely, so that situations like my brother and I could be addressed. When he suddenly passed away in later life I had already made my peace with him and we were glad we had put the record straight. In fact, in the last few years of his troubled life, most of which stemmed from his childhood, he would sit and discuss things that had been festering and we became really close.

By the time I was 21, I was working in a local firm of Solicitors where I worked for a lovely lady solicitor in the litigation department. It was so interesting to go to Court with my boss and see how it all worked but the job was quite harrowing as she dealt with divorce, matrimonial and custody cases.

All my friends were getting engaged and saving up to buy a house, with a view to marrying. It seemed if you were not married by the time you were 21 you had been 'left on the shelf' and people kept asking questions as to why you did not have a ring on your finger. I was 21 when I married Richard. My mother had tried to stop the marriage and even on my wedding day she told me in no uncertain terms that the marriage would never last. She resented spending all the money, but of course, it was the 'done thing' to have a big white wedding and frowned on by family and neighbours if it was not a lavish occasion. I was far too young and I would not encourage any children I might have to marry at this age. I had not really seen any of the big wide world, or been able to follow any of the dreams I might have had but this was how it was in those days.

I had a beautiful wedding and it was the last time my whole family would all be together, as aunts and uncles and especially my grandparents were 'getting on a bit'. I was extremely sad that two weeks before my wedding, my midwife grandma fell down and broke her wrist and went to a convalescent home to recover.

I really wanted her to be there, as she had always been there for me right from taking my first breath coming into the world and especially during the difficult teenage years when I went to live on my own. Unbeknown to my parents, I visited her every week and had dinner with her but my mother thought it best that she stay in the home, even though she was still pretty sprightly. On my way to the reception, I asked the driver of our wedding car to pass by the home and I got out the bridal car so my grandma could actually see me in my wedding dress from her window, so at least I saw her on my wedding day. After the wedding I made sure my wedding bouquet was delivered to her with some wedding cake, before we left on our honeymoon.

I continued working at the solicitors for the next seven years until leaving to have a baby, something else everyone kept on about, as if I had something wrong with me. Making comments such as 'not having any family yet' like it seemed to be a normal requirement to fall pregnant and have a baby within two years at the most of getting married. However, with everyone having babies, I realised that I was in fact getting 'broody' so we bought an Old English Sheepdog puppy and named it Benny. Although I loved him dearly, taking him out for walks with everyone admiring the 'Dulux dog' it didn't really fill the gap.

Now I was pregnant, I could not believe how big I was getting as I had never weighed so much, I had put on over 3st and could not remember what my feet looked like. When I went for my final check-up, I was told by the doctor they could hear two heartbeats and I may have been carrying twins!!

All I could think of as I walked to X ray, I was too big to even think of getting up on the trolley. Obviously, no ultrasound scans in 1977, as they pushed a ruler down my Bridget Jones pants to stand me upright, was my beautiful silver cross pram which only had one hood and I had only knitted one set of each of the baby clothes.

Luckily, after being in labour for hours, on the 14th January 1978 I gave birth by caesarean to a beautiful baby girl weighing in at 9lbs 8oz. I called her, of course, Elizabeth. When I came round from the anaesthetic, all I could see was this huge baby laying next to me in the plastic crib. All I remembered was being wheeled out of the delivery suite to the operating theatre and I must have been asleep for days. When I awoke, I felt to see if the bump had gone and to my horror all I could feel were flowers. When I looked down, there were bouquets of flowers laying across me - did they think I was dead and they were laying me out! I had to find my voice otherwise they might not realise I was in fact still alive. I would try and attract the next nurse I saw and put them straight she was alive but maybe not kicking.

The nurse laughed when I told her I was still alive and it appeared they were so busy that they had not had time to put the flowers in water and left them there until I finally woke up and could see them. How long had I been asleep? My daughter had been born four hours previously and yes she looked like she was already three months old. Giving birth by caesarean was quite a shock as no one had ever explained about the operation, I had just assumed I would give birth normally. No one imparted this information at the childbirth classes my ex Husband Richard and I had attended and he thought bathing a baby was going to be tricky!!

When the consultant visited me later, he told me 'better luck next time', as he tweaked my toes at the bottom of the bed. He must have been joking, 'next time', there was definitely not going to be a next time, I was closed for business in that department. After all, he did enough complaining about being called out from his bed in the hospital in the early hours of the morning saying "Are you still here?," as if I had any choice in the matter "And what are my options?." I remember saying " I just want this baby out now," although at one stage I did think of taking to my heels and running away. How did my mother go through this four times and deliver normally and how could my grandmother have done this as a job every day. Elizabeth was definitely going to be an only child.

I remember looking at her and thinking she was the most beautiful baby I had ever seen, loads of dark hair and blue eyes and so wide awake, unlike her mother, she had definitely been here before. I could not believe I had actually given birth somehow to this huge baby when I am so small, she was like a toddler and in the nursery, I could pick her out quite easily as the other babies were so tiny.

However, as they say, you soon forget as everyone told me the second baby would be easier and I gave birth normally to a beautiful baby boy, whom we called Max, weighed in at a mere 8lbs as he was induced three weeks early. He would have been 10lbs if he had gone full term - I do not think so, I thought as it made my eyes water just thinking about it. I was advised that every baby I had would be bigger, so would have to be delivered early - hence I decided to stop at two having wanted four children originally as I had my 'pigeon pair'.

I was so pleased both grandmas lived long enough to see Elizabeth as I could see from midwife grandma it brought back so many memories of when I was little. Both my grandmas were 96 when they finally passed away which was a really good age. It was not until recently when my sister Barbara and I were looking on Ancestry for details of our family tree did we uncover the secret that midwife grandma was not actually our biological grandma. We managed to uncover some details of our mother's birth mother but unfortunately due to our mother's advanced age she was unwilling, or unable to give us any further information and so this went with her to her grave. However, midwife grandma will always be my real grandma whatever we uncover.

CHAPTER 8

These were the happiest days of my life when my children were little and I lived in a small village in East Sussex with Benny, my Old English Sheepdog, who was amazed at these two new additions to the family. I was reminded of Peter Pan's Nana, as he was extremely protective of the children and often used to sit in the middle of them in the car, all 8 stone of him. The children loved him and he loved them especially when it was treat time.

When the children were 3 and 1 respectively, we moved for Richard's work and I could not believe I was going to live in the place where I had spent many of my happy childhood years. I had always promised myself that if I ever had any children, I would make sure they learned to swim at a very early age and I made sure I took them to swimming lessons. They were both unaware of my fear of the water and became really good swimmers.

Whilst the children were at school, I decided to return to part time work at a firm of local solicitors. I had never done conveyancing before but I soon found my way around the wordy leases that no-one ever understood and when clients came in were completely bewildered by all the jargon. I realised that although the competition was fierce, if I won the quotes, then there was money to be made and to that end my boss, who loved the horses, left me to see the clients.

The exchanges and completions were always fraught and I soon realised why getting a divorce, buying a house and dying, were three very stressful experiences for most people. I was always pleased when Friday morning came and all the completions had successfully taken place. It wasn't always plain sailing, someone would either go off with the keys, try to move in before the other person had moved out, or even worse the monies were not released in time. People used to scream and shout, very often breaking down in tears and saying they were never moving again, it was so stressful.

Memories of my own school days came flooding back to me when I saw how very unhappy my own children were at school and with a much better job, I might be able to afford to send them to a really lovely nearby school. My father had always impressed upon me the need for a really good education and so I took the children to see a local prep school. I knew as soon as I drove down the driveway that this was the right school for them and I had to move them as the advantages were amazing in all aspects. Once we looked around the school, I knew they would be happy, which they were. I would just have to find the money from somewhere as I could not send one without the other but I would need to up my game and find a better-paid job.

I saw the advertisement for a position in a local Government Office and as I had always wanted to go back into some form of litigation, I thought that with the increase in money and a change of job this would fit the bill. How wrong could I have been, it was one of the worse moves I had ever made. The office was only five minutes up the road and on a good day, I would be able to walk and save petrol. At the interview I was asked for all my school certificates, first stumbling block, where were they all?

Last time I saw the certificates they were in the family house in Tonbridge in my father's office maybe. I spoke to my father who confirmed that in the floods of 1968 all our personal belongings were destroyed and it brought back memories of that awful day.

The certificates had to be obtained with great difficulty from the governing boards but once received I started work. I should have known from the first day that this was not the job for me, as having done the six weeks of training I knew I was not going to be very popular imposing these measures on peoples lives. There was no pleasing anyone unlike the Courts, where I had seen so many maintenance orders discussed and implemented in a fair way, I was required to take over these court orders and in many cases increase the maintenance being paid. In many cases it was heartbreaking and I found the job harrowing, it was so tied up in red tape with so little leeway.

I was really able to relate in many ways to many of my cases as I had always thought, somewhat naively, my marriage would last forever and I would never be in the position of getting a divorce. When people used to say to me "You just don't understand what it's like" I wanted to say to them "Actually I do understand what you are going through," not only from my previous job but now from personal experience. I used to look at my friends who were with the same partner celebrating their 25th anniversary with great envy but somehow things don't always pan out the way you want them to, so I did understand how they were feeling.

I dreaded going into work and hated what I was doing to some of the families. All I had to do was hang in there and just bide my time as my children were nearly through school. Then to my dismay, all overtime ceased at the weekends which sent alarm bells in my head as I would need to find a second job, so I took a job cleaning.

CHAPTER 9

One Saturday morning I arrived at the caravan site and did not know what to expect. The other girls eyed me up suspiciously and as they worked in twos and were used to the speed the caravans had to be cleaned for new occupants, no one wanted to work with a 'newbie' like me so I was always last to be chosen. I felt I was back at school waiting to be picked for the netball team and you were last to be picked.

Begrudgingly I was given a list with one of the other girls, cleaning started at 10 am and all caravans had to be ready for 2 pm for the new occupants. I could not believe the state of some of the caravans, mine seemed to be worse than anyone else's and the other ladies worked so quickly and were finished long before me.

It had to be done and time would pass and maybe they might warm to me. However, one day I did find out why they were so cautious of me. I was so poorly on this particular day and one of the girls felt sorry for me and it turned out someone knew where I worked and they thought I was spying for the benefits agency, which of course was totally untrue. Despite reassurances that this was not my intention and trying really hard to be friendly, I never did fit in and at the end of the summer I had to give the job up as I needed an operation.

I would be off work for six weeks - bliss. When I returned to work, they had moved my desk yet again. This is something that happened on a regular basis as I had already moved onto most floors and around the office into different teams. There was absolutely no continuity and this took valuable time from dealing with the cases and the dreaded stats.

This move, however, was to be the start of a great friendship with a girl called Janine, who had also experienced some of the difficulties I was facing with my divorce. The other person I was friendly with was called JP, who was later on to play a huge role in my future life, little did I realise at the time.

Janine and I were not friends at first, in fact, Janine found me far too bright and noisy but gradually she realised that this was to cover what was really going on inside my home life. I invited Janine home for lunch one day and she soon got the picture that all was far from well and that I was merely covering it up by putting on a brave face.

The divorce was extremely difficult and I felt unable to tell anyone how bad things really were so I shunned away from my friends, as I felt so ashamed of how much debt I was now in through no fault of my own. I did not want my children to realise how bad things were and to have to leave their home at this difficult time was unthinkable. I would have to raise the money somehow to pay off all the debts and to pay my ex-husband Richard off that enabled me to keep the house. I was afraid every time the doorbell rang and I just wished sometimes that the post would just stop arriving as every day brought more and more disastrous bills.

Although I hated the job, at least going to work gave me some peace from my home life. It was during one of the weekends when working overtime I was flicking through the paper and I came across an advertisement from one of the big airline companies. They were recruiting for cabin crew and they had extended the application age to 45. I read the criteria and it appeared on the surface that I met the requirements - all I had to do was make a phone call. As Janine said, "What do you have to lose, it is only a telephone call." 'Why not' I thought to myself, my life seemed to be going from bad to worse. This could be my chance and I could give it a try and perhaps dig the tunnel out of this dreary job. I might not be successful but if I never tried I would always wonder what might have been.

I answered all the questions and seemed to meet the airline's initial requirements and was absolutely amazed to be asked to attend a hotel near London for an initial interview. Recent photographs were required and I just hoped the stress of the past months hadn't put my weight and height beyond the required limits. When the paperwork arrived I realised there were very strict guidelines about this (luckily not so nowadays!!) and as I was just 5ft 3" tall, the minimum height required, I knew I would need to lose a few pounds.

As Janine and I were driving up to London, I could not believe what I might be embarking upon and the whole process seemed extremely daunting. On arrival, I saw all these beautiful, slim and much younger girls and I suddenly realised the enormity of this venture. Suddenly it was too late as someone was calling my name and the process of selection was about to start. Nowhere to run and hide I thought, might as well give it a chance, what really had I got to lose and they could only reject my application.

Shoes had to be removed and hair flattened, I realised I need not have bothered to backcomb my hair up as the next second a slide rule came down on top of my head, I just made the height! Now for the tricky part, the weight. I wished I had resisted all those cream teas and pieces of cheese! I breathed in hoping that if I held myself in it might make the difference. Funny how we always think this will make us weigh less. I watched with trepidation as the black indicator moved past the numbers and willed it to stop as 8 stoneish loomed up.

Luckily I was told to move on to the next stage and breathed a huge sigh of relief. I was acutely aware that many of the smaller girls who were wearing stilts for shoes and had backcombed their hair within

35

an inch of its life had not proved successful and had fallen at the first hurdle and were told to leave.

What hard luck I thought, to fail just because you were too short. However, as it was later explained, the height requirement was because of opening and closing the overhead locks on board the aircraft and reaching the safety equipment. It was not thought to be becoming to be seen climbing up on the seats in front of passengers - does not give a good impression and especially in a restricted skirt!!

We were told that although high-heeled shoes would be worn on boarding, flat shoes would be required to change into once the doors were put into automatic. If the slides were deployed at this stage and the aircraft had to be evacuated, then high-heeled shoes might tear the slide and cause it to deflate - not a good idea with hundreds of passengers going down including yourself. Evidently, all would be explained if we were successful but it seemed a long-haul from any of these requirements at this stage.

Passports had to be shown and of course, a criminal record check would have to be undertaken, as if flying longhaul, a visa for entry and working in the USA would have to be obtained. This would not be available if it was found that you had a criminal record. With the first stage over now it was the long wait to see if I would be called for the second stage.

The wait seemed endless and after two weeks had passed I had disappointingly convinced myself that there was no way I was going to be called back. For the time being I must put this on hold and maybe apply again later, although the two year wait would almost put me out of the age restriction.

So it came as the biggest surprise ever to receive the telephone call requesting that as I had been successful, I was invited to attend for stage two. What to wear - I could not wear the same suit as it might be the same people interviewing me, although why would they remember me in particular but they may have taken notes of personal presentation. "No" something different it must be, I could not afford to lose any 'brownie points'.

As I arrived with all the other candidates, I was aware that once again they were all a lot younger and as I sat down behind my desk, I felt it was like being back at school but it was such a long time ago for me - the others looked as though they had only just left school. Still, here goes I thought. The maths was first, answer as many questions in the alloted time, which seemed to pass very quickly and everyone seemed to finish a long time before me. Later on, I learned that it was accuracy rather than speed they were looking for, as I would find out at my final interview.

English was next and then a language test would be taken once the candidate had been successful and a badge with the language spoken would be worn.

Lunch seemed to come round all too quickly and then everyone was able to chat about how it all went. Some of the others had no concerns and were so full of confidence. I did not remember putting those answers down on my paper, did I do the same paper I wondered. It made me nervous just thinking about it now, anyway I should not be eavesdropping, what was done was done.

Results were back, some of the candidates had failed and those that had passed the tests were put into groups. Perhaps I had not done so badly as I envisaged, I had not thought that some of the others might have been wrong and me right. I must try and have more faith in myself but my circumstances had taken away any confidence I used to have.

The different groups were given a scenario, ie. if you were stranded on a desert island how would you cope, whilst being observed as to how each candidate would contribute to their survival. Some people instantly had to take charge and made sure their voices and opinions were heard above everyone else.

It was extremely difficult for me, who was normally quite vocal, to enter into the discussion, as I was acutely aware of being observed as there seemed to be a lot of notes being taken. There were obviously leaders and followers but what was the correct path, they should surely come together to discuss a plan on which they were all agreed. I was suddenly aware of a lady much the same age as myself, standing next to me. She confided in me that she didn't think she had done well as it appeared everything we suggested was somehow overlooked and discounted. It was lovely to have a coffee and chat with someone who was feeling the same as myself.

On the drive home, I tried not to be disappointed as after all my application was a long shot. To have been given a job in a field where I had very little experience, apart from going abroad on holiday and having never even worked in the travel industry and at my age was, I suspected, quite an ask. Nevertheless, when the letter arrived advising that I had not been successful this time, it came as a bitter blow as by now my job and my home life had become unbearable, I must dig the tunnel deeper and get out somehow.

It was on one of my darkest days that I received a letter from the airline company inviting me to apply for a ground crew job on the check-in desks at Gatwick Airport. At least this might be a fresh start and my way out and I would be able to gain valuable experience and may be more successful next time a cabin crew vacancy came up. The down side was the six week course was on a fail or pass basis. Once I had given up my job, failure was not an option and there was no way back, I had to apply and maybe think about the consequences later.

Why did I always doubt my own abilities? I think its called practice what you preach, as I was always telling my children to think positively and there was no such word as 'can't' and yet here I was doing just that.

On the drive up to Gatwick I contemplated the long drive of one and a quarter hours each way against the five minutes it took me at present from my front door to the office but I hadn't even got the job yet.

At the interview, it was explained that this position would give me valuable information as to how the airline industry worked as a whole, which in turn would put me in good stead when the cabin crew recruitment drive took place again. I already had good customer service skills which were an essential requirement in the job and I would have to get used to different shifts, including lates and night shifts. Also, how did I feel about the drive as the first early shift was 5 am and I would need to be at the airport at 4.45 am to start work, which would mean getting up at 2.30 am. I needed to have a very difficult discussion with my now teenage children but I so wanted to give this a try should I be successful.

Janine and JP, who had both become a very important part of my life, helped tremendously all through this difficult period and told me to take the chance and that I could do this. I was not sure at this time, with my children being in their last years at school, could I take a risk from a nice secure civil service job to a job in an industry I knew nothing about and much further away from home.

I knew I was treading into unknown and very dangerous waters, which were never a very good idea for a non swimmer! However, tunnel dug, my leaving party was wonderful and I really enjoyed every minute of it whilst hearing my head of department saying how much I would be missed - yes right!! The gold chain and locket I was given by all my colleagues were beautiful and wherever I went I would always have a picture of my children hanging around my neck to remind me how lucky I was to have them. Everyone from my department came to the dinner and then went on clubbing, even my own children turned up, although my son had asked me not to embarrass him by talking to him and letting anyone know I was his 'mother'. After all having a mother when you are a teenager is just the worse thing. The person who brought you into the world, fed and clothed you, supplied money when things got a bit short, was a general taxi service, was not to be acknowledged, always makes me laugh as it seems to apply to all generations.

It turned out I was able to fund the whole of his evening and as I told him I did not want people knowing I have teenage children and cramping my style. "Yes right Mother" he replied, as if I was past going out past 9oclock and needed a late night pass.

This was the first time I had met JP socially and I suddenly became very aware that this would be the last time I would see him. It would be very strange not working with him every day and I realised I would miss seeing him but there was definitely no way I was going to start any romantic relationship at this stage, or in fact ever at all, I had to get out of my present one first.

JP must have realised the same, as he put his arms around me and we started dancing, I suddenly became more aware of him other than just as a work colleague. He was a lot younger than me and why would he be remotely interested in someone older, with children and going through a very acrimonious and costly divorce. Not exactly a recipe for a romantic relationship I thought.

At the end of the evening, however, JP asked if he wrote to me and asked me out for dinner would I consider going. There was so much ahead of me I was not sure this was a good idea, but heyho, maybe I would think about it, if he ever actually made contact. I thought once I had left work this would probably never happen, a case of out of sight out of mind and who writes letters these days - I still have the letter!!

CHAPTER 10

On the Monday morning I set off at 6 am just to make sure I was not late for the first day of training and as I drove past my old office, I wondered what on earth I had done. 110 miles round trip and not home until 7 pm as to just 5 mins down the road but nothing ventured nothing gained.

It was not easy to find the hangar where I was to spend a good deal of my time with the airline but I just headed for the noise of the aircraft landing and taking off and I knew I could not be far away. I always marvelled at how such a huge lump of metal with all that luggage and passengers could possibly thunder down the runway and lift off with such ease and grace, changing course and climbing high until it disappeared into the clouds. I was even more determined that I would meet the challenges ahead of me and one day I would be in my cabin crew seat and taking off or landing on one of these aircrafts.

I entered the security gates, explained I was there for airline training and the man on the intercom told me to park up and come to the portacabin to sign in. I was soon to realise from now on I would not be allowed anywhere on the airport without strict security clearance and temporary passes were issued. This procedure would be adopted every morning whilst I was in training.

When I arrived at the cafe, other trainees started to arrive and all looking as apprehensive as I felt. We were soon collected by the trainers, who would be with us for most of the training and taken to the classroom. One of the older trainees came and asked if she could sit next to me and I was quite relieved when she said how nervous she was. Her name was Vivien and as I found out she was around my age and just as nervous; we remained friends throughout the course.

Just as I envisaged, the tutors arrived all immaculately dressed in their uniforms. I could not wait to get my uniform and felt quite childlike in my anticipation of the visit to uniform stores but this was a long way off, if at all possible. This was unlike the days of going to the school shop to be fitted out with a school uniform which I would grow into, this uniform would at least fit perfectly and look so prestigious.

They then went around the room and we were asked individually to give our names and brief details about ourselves, I dreaded this. The younger members were all eager and I was rehearsing what I was going to say so I did not become tongue-tied or gabble on, my turn approached all too quickly. I soon realised that my children were nearly as old as some of the other candidates. I took a deep breath and introduced myself and said I was in my forties and had two teenage children, Elizabeth and Max. I also explained that I also had a ' foster daughter' Alex, who I had looked after long term as she was the best friend of my daughter and had been living with me while her mother recovered from an accident.

I thought the 55 miles I travelled each way was far enough so when some of the other trainees said how far they were going to travel every day, ie. Birmingham and Hampshire, my journey was just around the corner. However, as the days and weeks went by with all the homework, some of the others started to feel the strain and decided to find accommodation together nearer the airport, especially for the early mornings and late finishes. I soon found I became the mother to the group as some of the other candidates became extremely weary and when tiredness crept in, this made them tearful.

We were put into groups and would work together on different tasks but predominantly focused on customer service. "What would you do if a plane was delayed due to mechanical failure, or weather"? Weather seemed easier to deal with as passengers would, in some ways, accept that we had no control over weather conditions, well that is some passengers. There appeared to be passengers who would even imply that although the aircraft had below the visibility to take off, or the snow was too thick, they still had to be at their meeting!

In general, I began to realise that once I put on the uniform I would be a target for every question imaginable. It would be no good hiding under the long navy blue gaberdine mac!

I soon learned to fuel my car nearer home or on a rest day, as trying to refuel on my way home in uniform was a definite target for trying to get information of all sorts. "Is the plane to Nairobi tonight on time and how full is it?" the questions would come thick and fast.

Realisation of what was to come, as experienced by the tutors, soon set in and homework every night when I had the drive from hell in the rush hour meant I was burning the midnight oil. Why did places not all have a simple three letter code like MAN for Manchester, not MRU for Mauritius, NBO for Nairobi and LAX for Los Angeles to name but a few of the easier airport codes to remember. Whole trees would have been cut to enable me to take the hundreds of notes I had made just to remind me for the exams ahead.

It seemed to be I had only just closed my eyes when the alarm was going off, it surely could not be 4.30 already. Showering, hair and make-up done to an immaculate standard were always challenging to leave the house at 5.45 am silently. Closing the front door and starting a diesel car in silence also proved tricky, I did not turn my headlights on until I had rolled out of the drive, even then the noise and the lights seems to illuminate the whole road like a Christmas tree.

Mary Middleton

The drive to the airport was spent revising and trying to dodge every animal that decided it was a good idea to jump out in front of the car. I swerved to avoid the rabbits who ran out into the road before running back to the side, it was like they had some sort of death wish. Badgers were a whole new ball game, they would just stop defiantly and glare as if to say "Well go around me" and if you hit one it was like hitting a rock, so was to be avoided at all costs, likewise deer. I hated hitting any of the wildlife and would do anything to avoid these confrontations, luckily there was room for error with not much other traffic on the road at that ungodly hour.

As usual, everyone met in the canteen for coffee and to compare notes ready for the tests, it was just like being back at school. With the tests over it was time to enter the world of online check-in. It was scary to think that one day the system would be live and I would be inputting details of passengers, destinations, even worse making sure their bags went with the right person and to the correct destinations.

This was a very serious part of the whole procedure as obviously passengers and bags had to both go on the same flight, as it was a security issue if not and would result in disciplinary action. If it happened too frequently, a more serious procedure would be put in place, like collecting your P45.

There were so many things to remember, passengers names, passports being in date and visas obtained for some countries, as failure to make sure all the paperwork was correct would lead to the airline being fined and the passengers being sent straight back home. How many of them, as there could be large parties, how many children and what ages, how many bags, pushchairs, dogs in a box (that was definitely going to be a nightmare) likewise wheelchairs with all types of batteries and guns going for big game hunting. I just hoped they would not appear in my queue too soon.

It was extremely daunting with the thought of being on a check-in desk with real passengers, all eagerly hoping to be going on their holidays, sitting in seats together, bags having gone down the belt correctly tagged, all within two hours. I hoped it would just be business people going to Manchester for the day with no bags in my queue, but I should be so lucky.

The final exam day had arrived. It seemed like yesterday we had started, the six weeks had gone so quickly. I was just about to go into the exam room, when I received a frantic call from my son, saying that the bailiffs were at the door with a summons to seize goods for outstanding debts. I was devastated and was not sure what I could do from so far away. I really had no choice but to contact my friend Janine and hope that she might be able to fend the bailiffs off until I got home.

This was not a good start, I just knew I had to forget about everything and just concentrate on this final important exam but as soon as I logged into the online computer my mind went blank, the names and places were a blur. I struggled on, conscious that I was being observed by the examiners and I was actually glad when the time was up and I could get up and leave the room. I felt, and must have looked, terrible as everyone was looking most concerned. 'Was everything alright', I recall being asked.

I hardly remembered the drive home and wondered what would I find. Janine was waiting for me with the bailiff who had returned and taken everything apart from items that belonged to the children and I. They would be back for the car as the car was actually registered in Richard's partner's name and neither of them could be found, they had conveniently disappeared.

I was at rock bottom with no job, no car and now the building society were going to repossess the house as well, this was not going to be easy to hide from the children.

My mobile rang and it was the airline office, they wanted to see me in the morning and I feared the worst. I did not think I could face the others, as we had become very close having spent the last six weeks together, I feared sympathy at the moment would just make me burst into tears. Having passed their exams the others would be going to the uniform stores to have their uniforms fitted but there was so much to sort out at home - the dream was over, so near and yet so far.

I decided I would have to go to the office, even if it was just to say thank you and goodbye. The drive was terrible and with a heavy heart, I parked the car for the last time, swiped my pass which I knew would have to be given up and made my way to the office.

Luckily all the other trainees were in class, the strain was beginning to show. When the trainers confronted me as to why I had failed the exams, which I should have passed easily, I broke down and had to explain what was happening at home.

They were extremely sympathetic and had realised something was very wrong, as they knew I was more than capable of passing all the exams. After a lot of discussion it was agreed, in these extenuating circumstances, they would make an exception and I would be allowed to continue with the others and retake the exam, but this was unusual and if I failed again that would be the end. Could I put my home life aside and concentrate enough to get through this?

When I rejoined the group, they were so pleased to see me, I was quite taken aback; I explained I had a crisis at home that I had to deal with.

Five bad points at any stage in the six weeks would mean leaving the course and all that work would have gone to waste. It was extremely expensive to train each one of us. If we received five points we would be out, these varied between being late for class (even if we had been held up on the motorway, we should have left earlier) to taking time off for sickness. However, I do not think anyone wanted us to fail as we were a really lovely group of people.

Once we had been taken on, the job would only be a temporary position for six months until we proved that we were able to cope with the job. Any lateness, including time off for sickness, would be taken into account when offering a permanent position. I realised not everyone was suitable and would be kept on, which was extremely daunting as I no longer had a job to go back to.

CHAPTER 11

Going to uniform stores with the others was just wonderful and being fitted with this prestigious uniform. Even the handbag, gloves and pashmina were beautiful and very expensive. The bowler type hat was very rigid and had metal around the brim to keep its shape but I didn't care as I loved it all. The navy blue gaberdine mac reminded me of school days as it was so long it nearly reached my ankles, good thing I would be wearing high heeled shoes.

The uniform had to be worn strictly in accordance with the Uniform Standards Booklet and there was always someone watching or coming round the corner when I was racing home. The hat had to be worn at all times, including on the check-in desks, to and from the car park, in fact, any time when visible to the public. The raincoat had to be completely buttoned up and even the pashmina had to be correctly folded across the body in a certain way. No folding it like Rupert the Bear under your chin and definitely no running, only gliding!

I soon learned that if I looked calm and collected, the passengers would feel that everything was under control. If they saw you were anxious then they would know something serious might be going on. Smile at all times and always be the fountain of all knowledge, even at 4.30 in the morning!!

Hair had to be worn off the collar, tied in a bun or french pleat and preferably up with navy or black scrunchies and hair held in place with brown or black clips. Make-up likewise had to be immaculate and the lipstick and nail varnish had to be the required red colour.

The make-up demonstration by a leading beauty company on how to apply the different products was amazing. As most of it was done in the early hours of the morning and in not always good light, some of the hints and tips were invaluable. Foundation was required due to the strong lights, no-one wants to see staff sitting on desks looking anaemic. Likewise, you don't want to end up looking like a clown, especially with the red lipstick, which was something I wasn't keen on or had ever worn before.

It was such fun as the guys in the group enjoyed the make-up demonstration as much as the ladies, although all tattoos had to be covered with plasters, no visible piercings and no facial beards, unless it was a religious requirement. Only one wedding and engagement ring and wrist watch, no other jewellery could be worn and this caused a lot of discussion within the group.

When the demonstration was over I was delighted when each person was given a beautiful package of the products used, this was going to be challenging turning up every morning looking like a model, but I knew I would rise to the occasion. Luckily my hair was fairly long and with a quick swish of the brush and a very forgiving navy blue ribboned hair clip and hairspray, this would take less than five minutes. The make-up would be a little more difficult as I did not want to look as though I was entering the circus!!

I obtained so much useful knowledge from the training about different cultures and diversities that I was unaware of but I would need to know this so as not to offend and be aware of special requirements. I would need to learn the different types of meals and their codes on the system so passengers had the right meal on their flights.

The most difficult to order at the last minute were Kosher meals as they have to be ordered 48 hours beforehand due to the special requirements, whereas most other special meals can be ordered 24 hours before. Vegetarian food was much easier as there was usually this option on board anyway but the backup catering truck very often could be recalled and extras were taken on board.

Any special requirements including meals, wheelchair assistance to and from the gate had a code which had to be remembered and entered onto the system, as you did not want a passenger left in the lounge and missing their flight.

Many children passed through the airport and many of them were from boarding schools. When the school bus arrived at the airport, the children were handed over to the "Aunties" who would look after them in a special lounge and make sure they arrived on time at the aircraft. These children had done this on many occasions and really did not need, or even want assistance but in those days it was a requirement. The airline did not want them getting lost, end up arriving late to the gate, or missing the flight completely.

As time went by and cut backs were made, this service was withdrawn and I missed the company of the 'Aunties' as we obviously got to know them really well and they were so lovely.

With all the excitment of putting the information into practise, I had forgotten one very important fact, I had not actually passed the final exam before being let loose on the live system. So it came as rather a surprise when I was called upstairs just before finishing the course and told not to be nervous, which always puts the fear of god into me. Its like saying 'Now this won't hurt' from the person just about to give you an injection. No of course it won't hurt them but its not to too comfy when you are the person just about to have the needle put in your unsuspecting arm, as I soon found out when I had to go to the Health Centre to have some of my injections brought up-to-date.

However, I knew in my heart of hearts that I would be required to pass the final exam, so I was taken into a side room with one of the tutors to complete the test. With all the information I had received I should be able to complete this and as the test was launched, the time started. I became totally engrossed, just myself and the computer and nothing else mattered now. I could feel that the tutor was monitoring the system to see how everything was going but she gave nothing away. Time up, I could do no more, I had checked and rechecked my answers as my tutor stood up and came over to check my score. I could see she was smiling. Was this a good sign, I hope so. I did not want the fail or pass key to be pressed for fear of what it might say, but as I held my breath the key was pressed and up came the words Congratulations you have passed.

I was now able to go and join the others and start work on Check-In at the airport on Monday morning on the live system and to put into practise all we had been taught over the last six weeks.

It was frowned upon to have any prejudice against anyone, if you had any strong feelings, we were told we should keep these to ourselves and quite rightly everyone should be treated with the same respect. Many of my new work colleagues and friends were from all over the world and a large amount of the male crew were gay. I had no preconceived ideas really of how this would work but I found the gay guys were lovely to work with, funny, kind and considerate and from them I had a much better understanding of the gay community, something I had not experienced before and I am lucky that I still remain good friends with some of them.

All this being said I was teased about the way I spoke and acted - why is it people assume that if you come from Essex and are called Sharon you immediately speak a certain way and everyone wants to call you Shaz or Shazza and that we are completely brainless? Even worse if you went to a convent together with the above "you know what convent girls are like." "No I don't know what I am supposed to be like" but I disliked having my name shortened and once people got to know me they know I am definitely not a Shazz or Shazza and guess what, I am one of many Essex people who do have a brain. My friends and colleagues throughout my life at the airport used to say "Now does she look like a Shazza" - although I am never really sure what a Shazza does look like!

I never really liked the taste of alcohol, much to everyone's amusement but never admitted it when I was growing up. However, when going out with work colleagues I realised I didn't have to drink to have fun. I was always popular as everyone knew I would be driving them home and it caused great hilarity that I came from a family of big drinkers and I was teetotal. As I travelled to work so early in the morning, I had been stopped by the police and asked if I had been drinking three times!! Luckily, because I was in uniform, I was only actually breathalysed once. I was not sure how I was going to cope with the teetotal part if I became cabin crew as I knew I would have to go to a wine and champagne tasting day and experience and recommend the different vintages and grapes to passengers in Club and First Class some of whom would wine and champagne connoisseurs. If I was successful in becoming cabin crew I would need a good understanding in this area. For the time being this was still on the back burner.

Perhaps my days at the convent with the eagle-eyed nuns always pulling me up about wearing the uniform correctly had in some ways stood me in good stead for the wearing of this new uniform. However, this uniform was so smart I wanted to wear it with pride and just putting it on ready for work made me feel a different person and I loved it.

Wearing the uniform I soon realised I was in the public eye and soon became aware I needed to make sure I knew everything about the airport, including what time the Oxford bus left and from where!! I was stopped in supermarkets and asked if I knew which aisle the rice was in and questions like was the Nationwide open on Saturday mornings. It was completely bizarre and I was always amazed at the different questions people would come up with.

One day before Christmas, I had rushed into Sainsburys on my way home to grab a few essentials. When I reached the end of the store, a lady came running breathlessly up to me and thrust some money into my hand, as I queued at the bakery counter. Imagine my surprise when she said, "I am so glad I caught up with you, I missed you at the door and I wanted to put some money into your tin." It turned out she thought I was a member of the Salvation Army who had been singing at the entrance of the store!! I cannot tell you how often I was put in funny situations by the public.

Even people who were at the very top of their profession, who quite obviously had a P.A. dealing with every eventuality, would turn up with their wife's passport not having checked this before just picking it up from the safe before jumping in the chauffeur driven car taking them to the airport. "Can I not travel on the passport and hope that no one will notice." Well, I think someone might firstly pick up the fact that it was a blonde haired lady in the photograph and sir had very little, if in fact no hair, might be a slight giveaway.

"I have to go to a very important meeting in Amsterdam and I must be there for 11 am to do something." A frantic call would be made to home where an unsuspecting wife would be summonsed to the safe and given the co-ordinates for the safe opening. Not an easy task when you were in bed and thinking you were going to have an easy day to be asked "four clicks to the right, three to the left" and still the safe remained locked.

So after much aggravation and blaming, after all, who was it who did not check the passport was the correct one, the safe was opened and the passenger's passport retrieved. The chauffeur was recalled from his, what he had thought at the time sedate journey home, but now was under pressure to 'step on it' and return home to collect said passport and return to the airport in time to catch the 11 am flight. Sir was lucky this time to make it with just moments to spare - this would be one of many near misses that I would have to deal with and not all would be that fortunate.

CHAPTER 12

How strange it felt as I drove past my old workplace just five minutes from home and now having scrape the ice off the car, I was preparing to make the one hour 15 minute journey to work. Life would never be dull again as I was soon to find out no two days were ever alike.

I was given a 'buddy' just to help settle in with the daunting task of going down the steps to a check-in desk, putting up the destination behind me and then turning to face the awaiting passengers. I was now on the live system and no room for any errors, I wanted to run at that precise moment.

Suzie, my buddy, told me to relax and make myself comfortable. As I opened the baggage belt and pressed the red button, it started to move and I knew I must really concentrate, check the tags before sending the bags down the belt into the depths below. I knew if I made a mistake I would have to close the desk, ring the loading department and ask them to hold the bag; something that was frowned upon and taken really seriously, especially if it delayed a flight.

I did not want to have a black mark and be called up in front of my manager, so accuracy was vital but speed was also important as all the passengers had to be checked in when the flight closed. FMU, the Flight Monitoring Unit, would deal with any problems that occurred during check in.

Suddenly there was a sea of faces in front of me, as the unsuspecting passengers saw me opening my check-in, swarmed over from another long check-in queue. They would be sorry when they found out it was my first day and extremely lucky to make tomorrow's flights, I thought. I just hoped there would not be too many families with pushchairs or loads of heavy bags or passport problems. Suzie explained to the passengers that it was my first day and some looked at me with sympathy and some I could feel looked at me thinking "trust us to choose this queue, we should have stayed where we were." Probably quite right.

The first bag had been put on the baggage belt, the tickets were correct and matched the passports and were checked in with seats. When I was absolutely sure the bags were tagged correctly, I cautiously pressed the red button and saw the bags move off down the belt, boarding passes handed over and passengers happily moving off to the Departure Lounge.

A huge sigh of relief as I realised I had checked my first passengers in, only the rest of the long queue to go but I was gradually settling into it and the time went by very quickly. I could not believe it when we heard footsteps coming down the steps behind us, two hours had passed so quickly and we were being relieved for a coffee break. So far so good and I had even spoken to FMU, which was very daunting depending on who picked up the phone and was in charge of that particular flight, as they were often very stressed depending on how the flight was going.

On occasions, there were problems with passengers bookings, whereby they were all packed and ready to fly on their holiday but the tickets were incorrect, the name on the ticket did not match their passport, the date on the ticket was incorrect or they had arrived on the wrong date. With the time changes in different parts of the world, this caused many discrepancies as to when passengers thought they would be returning, all of which was usually our fault!!

In the beginning whenever I saw a dog or cat in a box, I felt fear and dread, as I knew the check-in would take some time. The documentation would have to be correct as when an animal is going into the hold there has to be heat, otherwise the animal would freeze to death, as the cargo hold becomes extremely cold during the flight. Hence this is why stowaways don't survive, which is very sad. The animals, however, were a completely different ball game as they would be put in a metal cage where we had to make sure that they were able to stand up and turn round and even worse make sure they seemed to be happy. Is any cat or dog going to look happy shut up in a container having travelled by car, then transferred to a trolley, wheeled through a busy airport only to be looked at by me and the decision taken as to whether they looked 'happy'. Most of them looked far from happy but anyway how could I assess whether they looked happy or not? The pet owners were always very stressed.

Some passengers thought the containers would go down the baggage belt! They were always pleased when a call was made to the Animal Reception Centre who would take over the safe transportation of the animal to the aircraft, having checked the animal over to make sure they are fit to fly. Once an animal goes on board and the cargo door closed and it is dark, most animals settle down and go to sleep as they have no idea of time. The owners always worry more about their animals, quite rightly, and are quite frantic until they know whether the animal has been loaded onto the aircraft.

When checking in one day, I noticed that the backpack a young girl was wearing was leaking water. When I told her about this she told me it was probably from her best friend Archie and I expected this to be some fluffy teddy or dog. I suggested she had better check her water bottle as it may be leaking but I was in absolute shock and horror when she opened the rucksack, in a cardboard box, was a bowl of lettuce and leftover water and her best friend Archie was in fact a live tortoise. He definitely did not look happy as he poked his head out of his shell to see what all the commotion was about.

I had to explain to her that sadly she could not take Archie just in a backpack on board the aircraft. She said she thought he would be perfectly okay, as he would just go into his shell until they arrived at their destination. However, I had no choice but to call the Animal Welfare department to come and collect Archie. No one could believe it upstairs when I told them the problem as they had never had to deal with a tortoise going on holiday.

The Tel Aviv flight was always checked in with armed police in attendance, which was strange at first and the passengers were quite complex in their needs. The Orthodox Jews did not like any female contact and so they preferred to be checked in by a male member of staff which was not always possible, so when I first checked this flight in I became used to having their tickets and passports thrown at me. Likewise, they would not want to sit next to any females on board the aircraft which was extremely difficult to work out, neither be in sight of a television and they carried loads of excess baggage, usually books. There was always a lot of discussion about excess baggage and the cost involved.

I was very unaware of many aspects of the Jewish religion and being on check-in certainly gave me a better understanding of how it all worked so as not to offend them. I think when they saw I was an older person, they probably thought my menstruation days were over and I was probably safer to deal with.

The Saga flights were always easy to check in. The reps would arrive with a full passenger list with seats together already allocated which was so much easier. I really loved these flights, the passengers were nearly always very smartly dressed, with a lot of the men wearing Panama hats to shield their heads from the hot sun and they were usually taking the flight and going on to meet a cruise ship.

They would also carry quite a lot of baggage as evening dresses and dinner jackets would be packed, although most of the gentlemen would say they had very little compared to their wives. "Why do you ladies need to take so many shoes and handbags?" I perfectly understood why as one has to have a pair of matching shoes for all occasions and outfits, I am an avid shoe collector myself and always pack far too many pairs.

The Japanese were also a joy to check in. Again the reps, who were also the interpreters, came with the passenger lists with seats nearly always allocated and they were so precise and respectful. Each couple would come forward bow and hand over their tickets and passports with both hands and put their suitcases on the baggage belt.

The interpreter was always there to answer any questions and to help when it came to answering the security questions that every passenger was obliged to confirm they understood. "Did you pack your bags yourself" and "Has anyone asked you to carry anything that does not belong to you." Nearly all their luggage was matching for the whole group and the interpreter usually had a flag, which they held aloft so that they never lost of him or her. They always bowed at the end of the check-in and were just delightful people who never made any fuss.

If nothing else, I learned to be respectful to all passengers young or old, different religions, race and colour and I found the endless amount of knowledge I received, especially from my somewhat sheltered background, was totally amazing. I was never surprised with what might happen, every day was different and it was certainly never boring.

CHAPTER 13

After six months the Company decided that those of us who had stood the test of time, as a few of us had fallen by the wayside for one reason or another, would have to wait for another tzhree months. We would then be offered permanent contracts together with staff travel which I was really looking forward to having.

Staff travel meant that we had ten cheaper tickets a year, these were called hotlines, and after seven years of service we were entitled to free tickets for myself, my partner and any children under the age of 25, whereby we only paid the airport tax.

This day was the first of many days I would spend on check-in and as I became more confident, I was sent to the Club and First Class desks which were amazing. When working behind the desk, I never knew when I looked up who would be standing in front of me, stars of stage and screen, some of whom were really lovely and others not quite so lovely. It was always disappointing when someone I had admired arrived at the desk and was absolutely foul, whilst others were really lovely and just what I expected.

Beautiful luggage on mass would very often appear on the First Class check-in with very high profile passengers attached and at first, I found it difficult to ask the ladies to remove their full facial burkas/ niqabs to identify themselves against their passports, but of course, they were used to this procedure as they travelled so frequently.

I found it all fascinating, especially when I met my first celebrity. I was on my way to board the Edinburgh flight when I looked up and saw and heard this voice saying "Good Morning, how are you?." It was only the lovely Sean Connery, I would recognise that drop-dead gorgeous voice anywhere. I nearly dropped all my paperwork and became tongue-tied but managed to get "Wonderful thank you sir."

This was to be the first of many encounters with stars and personalities I would be lucky enough to meet whilst carrying out my job. I was thrilled and glad he was so nice, with the most stunning sparkling eyes but I was of course quite bias being a Bond fan.

The Departure Lounge Information Desk was a circular desk in the middle of the Lounge and was really challenging. It was nearly always busy, especially when flights were cancelled or delayed. It was like target practice, people would home in and crowd around the desk all shouting, swearing and generally all talking at once. I knew when sent to the Departure Lounge I would need to be fully armed with as much information as I could to placate passengers and was so glad that we had been taken on a familiarisation of the airport visit during our training. Otherwise, I knew I would be sending passengers in the wrong direction and to the incorrect gates. Remembering where all the shops were also challenging as the outlets seemed to be forever moving.

Food vouchers would need to be distributed and of course, people who were making an onward connection who, because of the delay, would miss their flight and had to be sorted out. Others just wanted to shout and scream, as if it was my fault but I soon came to realise that going to an airport was extremely stressful for many people.

I could understand their frustration but really some of the anger, when it was weather conditions, was completely unreasonable. Why would you want to take off in an aircraft when visibility was so poor, or the runway was covered in ice and snow, was beyond me. It seemed to me that when the front door was closed to leave for the airport, brains and sense of reason remained at home.

Weather was a big problem during the winter months and I did feel sorry for people with children as they had set off early and been expecting to be sitting on a sunny beach, not delayed in an airport for hours with fractuous children. You can only just have so much of the shops in the Departure Lounge and even duty free after hours of delay loses its appeal.

My previous job had of course prepared me for much of the abuse I had to take and completely irrational comments when flights went 'tech'. As I had already learned it was much easier to let the passenger vent off and then see what I could do to give as much information as I was able to find out. It was always the Company policy that the passenger is always right, yeah right!!

Certainly, I had no idea and I am sure passengers have no idea, just how much knowledge of the airport, geography and how it all works in just getting people checked in and away on their holidays.

Arriving to board a flight when any one of the above had occurred was always interesting. I just had to keep my wits about me, as I knew I must not let a passenger through into the seating area not having been accounted for on the system. This was later improved by a gate reader, which in most circumstances, was pretty accurate. Nevertheless with everything going on, it was sometimes inevitable that the headcount was incorrect and someone from the gate team would be required to go and check on board to see if that person had in fact already boarded. I always volunteered as I knew this was really where I wanted to be, one day I thought, as I watched the aircraft push back fully loaded with passengers more or less happy, or happy as they could be.

Seating was a major issue on a lot of flights, some days everyone wanted a window and next, then other days an aisle and next.

Passengers would be completely irrational about seats and refuse to move even if it meant a small child of, who bore no relation to them, was sitting next to them. They wanted to be in 18C and they would not agree to accommodate the family by moving to another comparable seat, despite having a screaming three year old next to them, totally illogical.

FMU, who actually had been dealing with the flight whilst it had been checked in, would do their best to try to accommodate everyone, but inevitably it was not always possible. Sometimes it was easier when we had all the passengers with us at the gate to see if a compromise could be reached, although there were time constraints so as not to delay take off.

Moving seats at the gate so that families would not be split up was extremely challenging and of course, most people, when they realise that sitting next to an unknown small child for even a small amount of time let alone a longhaul flight, was not the best start to their holiday and would agree to move seats.

The Orlando and the Tampa flights were always full of families who had saved for a long time and were going on a once in a lifetime trip to Disney. The excitement of these passengers, especially the children, eagerly awaiting visiting the Magic Kingdom to see Mickey was very special. So making sure all the families were sitting together was especially important as I knew this was a very special part of the trip for this was the beginning of their holiday. Everyone would heave a sigh of relief when these two particular flights were boarded and airborne. I used to marvel as I watched the 777 push back with all those people on board and all that luggage, just how the aircraft ever took off. Passengers would always query why they had to be at the airport two hours or more before the aircraft took off, but I can assure you the work that goes on behind the scenes from all departments is immense.

Mind you it was not only the checked-in luggage that was always the biggest problem on certain flights, the hand luggage that was brought to the gate was totally irrational and passengers would not be parted from it.

Some of the hand luggage was nearly as big as their checked-in luggage and we would watch with amusement as passengers tried to force their overweight bag into the scales. They would state that it was definitely sold to them as being the correct size whilst being unable to hardly lift the bag off the floor. Trying to prise these bags from passengers was always challenging and could result in a delay on the flight departing. If all the overweight bags were allowed on board, other passengers would not find space in the overhead lockers. The row raged on, both at the gate and on board.

I loved the Kingston, Lagos and Accra flights as the size of the luggage was huge and always challenging. The people were colourful and loved to haggle over the charges for excess baggage and I enjoyed the bartering that used to go on.

The packing and unpacking of baggage that went on at check-in was hilarious, I had never seen so much henna hair dye, it was like Boots in some of the bags; just how much can you pack in those red, white and blue raffia bags, it was amazing. Car parts of all descriptions, whole exhausts used to turn up in those bags and then have to be distributed to meet the weight allowance, which at that time was 32kgs in each of two bags.

The haggling over excess baggage made my day and a lot of passengers ended up wearing more clothes than they had started out with, including a most beautiful array of hats. I loved it and it was never dull as some of the disputes were quite fiery but a compromise was always the order of the day and a large amount of repacking.

Likewise, when the Nairobi flight was checked in during the early evening, the correct firearms documentation and suitable containers had to be completed for the guns for 'big game hunting'. Obviously they did not go down the baggage belt, nor arrive going round and round on the arrivals baggage collection belt.

I loved the challenge of seeing a passenger coming to the desk with smoke coming out of their ears and being able to help them. Some passengers were fraught, especially if they had been held up in traffic or parking the cars with the children arguing and hyper with excitement. By the time they arrived at my desk, only to find there were no seats together, would be the last straw and I really felt for them despite how angry they were. All I could do was try and sort this out and send them away to the Departure Lounge a little less stressed.

Silver card holders that thought they should be Gold and allowed into all the lounges, nervous passengers who decided at the last minute that they would not board the aircraft, to go even on their honeymoon, was all in a days work and I enjoyed it all, well most of it. I would be lying to say there were not days when the airport was heaving, it was extremely hot and nothing seemed to go right, when like every job I was glad when the shift ended.

The early mornings took some getting used to, getting up at 2.30 am for the 5 am shift but at least I would be home just after lunch. Lates were 2 pm til 10 pm followed the earlies and then of course the dreaded nights which meant 10 pm til 6 am and sleeping in the rest room once the last flight had been met and cleared.

The airport was really creepy late at night, as the lights only went on when the sensor picked up a presence and going down the jetties, especially a certain jetty at gate 63, was even worse having been told that one of the dispatchers had seen what he thought was a ghost. I did not want the same encounter so was always pleased when the aircraft came on stand, the passengers had alighted, I could swipe the doors closed and beat a hasty retreat back to the safety of the restroom. It is amazing I thought once someone has sown the seed of doubt. I never came across anything remotely untoward in all the time I was meeting late night flights, despite the terrible cold draughts that used to blow up the back stairs until the door was locked, at least I think that's all it was.

All of a sudden I realised I was beginning to get the hang of it all and everything was fitting into place, I stopped feeling going down onto check-in was so daunting, so when the chance of going up a grade from A3 to A4, I jumped at the chance. This would mean more responsibility especially at the boarding gate where if the flight was delayed, the delay would be put down to the gate team, in particular myself. Due to the large amount of money involved in a delayed flight, I would be called upstairs and have to account as to the reason for the delay.

Sometimes it would be a combination of problems but everyone would be trying to 'pass the buck' as bonuses were dependent on the number of flight delays and monies paid out but I reckoned I was up to the challenge and it would look good when I reapplied for cabin crew.

I decided to go for the interview, after all nothing ventured nothing gained. To my surprise, I was promoted to A4 which meant checking in passengers in the same way but I would be in charge at the gate when the aircraft was ready to board. Timing was of the essence and having to use the intercom to call passengers to the gate was really scary to start with as I knew my voice could be heard all over the airport. Firstly advising the passengers that the flight was now ready for boarding through the appropriate gate and then as time went on the calls had to become more urgent. "This is the last and final call for flight number which is in the last stages of boarding and preparing to depart."

It was always amazing that even when the above call was made, people would still be in the duty free shops and it was only when the names of passengers were called did it make them realise that they might miss their flight. The last and final warning which usually made them come running was "This is the very last and final call for passenger (NAME) travelling to (DESTINATION) please come immediately to Gate (NUMBER) as you are now delaying this flight and your bags are being identified and removed from the aircraft." This would nearly bring passengers running but, not always, some would still turn up at the gate and be surprised to see the aircraft pushing back without them, surprised that we had not waited for them.

Funny that they had not heard our numerous tannoy calls, but all the other hundreds of other passengers on the flight had managed to arrive on time!

From very early on I realised just when it was appropriate to have fun with passengers and when this would be inappropriate so one day at the gate we were just waiting for one passenger, quite a familar name I remember thinking at the time. I had made a tannoy call and we were all discussing whether this passenger was going to be the real Game Show Host or not, when we heard the footsteps of someone running. As the gentleman arrived at the gate and apologising profusely that he had gone to the incorrect gate he asked me if this was the correct gate for his destination and I replied 'It might be or would you like to take a 50/50 or phone a friend'. He laughed and said he would like a pound for every time someone had said that to him. He was absolutely lovely, much taller than I imagined albeit he was wearing a very large waxed raincoat which made him look much bigger but he was exactly as he appears on the TV and did not disappoint our expectations.

CHAPTER 14

I wished my homelife was going as well, my divorce seemed to be costing more and more money. In fact, I wished my solicitor would not speak to me as I could see the pound signs ringing up every time he spoke to me. Now due to the financial implications I faced, I would have the added costs of employing a barrister, mega money, but if I were not to lose everything I needed to employ someone who would be fighting on my side.

I had managed to persuade the building society that I could now afford an interest only mortgage. I had been promoted (hopefully) and could pay my ex-husband off and have sufficient monies to repair the house, which was now in a very bad state of repair. The outlay of money seemed to be never ending, if it wasn't solicitors it was the builders. I needed to buy a decent car as the travel to and from work was vital to be able to keep my job.

The bailiffs had taken the car on their last visit, so getting a car somehow was now a top priority. I hoped I would get the A4 position as it would give me some more money to play with and maybe take out a loan on a car, as due to the distance involved it could not just be an old banger.

On arrival at the airport one morning, I was called aside and to my amazement, was asked if I could 'buddy' one of the new entrants. It only seemed five minutes since I was in the same position and here I was 18 months later assisting a new recruit.

I could see how nervous he was and I remembered my first days on check-in, although the system had changed now. The floorwalkers monitored the queues and sent people to the different desks once they became free, which was a lot less daunting. It allowed any problems to be dealt with without having the pressure of people 'tutting' and loudly asking why this queue was taking so long compared to others.

Poor Jez, he looked panic-stricken with all the passengers in front of him as suddenly the system is live and making a mistake was not an option. I could tell how relieved he was when the morning passed by quickly and the sound of footsteps could be heard on the back steps which meant they were being relieved to go for a break. It brought back so many memories and seemed like yesterday this was happening to me.

Whilst on a break it came to light that Jez actually lived in the same town as me and in fact very close by, what a stroke of luck. It turned out if we could be put on the same line we would be able to share the journey to work. This could be a real result for me as people who shared cars were allowed in a staff car park nearer the airport - what a result for both of us.

It turned out that Jez disliked the journey as well, so he jumped at the chance of being able to car share as it would save on fuel and wear and tear on the cars. Perhaps my luck was changing at last I thought.

We were on an early shift one November morning, it was still dark and pouring with rain. I remembered the bright lights, looking to the right to see one of the Alpha food trucks coming onto the roundabout. When not laden they moved more quickly and I remembered Jez pulling up to let the lorry go first. All of a sudden there was a terrible bang, the radio came out of its casing and hit me, whilst my head ricochet backwards and forwards on the headrest.

The crack that came from my neck, together with the excruciating pain told me that this could be serious. As I opened the car door to be sick I could see Jez remonstrating with the owner of the car behind that had just smashed into the back of his virtually new car. Once they saw how sick I was they stopped arguing and came to assist me but I knew somehow all was not well, the pain in my neck and back was terrible.

It was a member of cabin crew from another airline, who had just heard that she had been made redundant and was just not concentrating. I could see how distressed she was when she saw how much damage she had inflicted both on the car and to ourselves. She just kept saying 'I am so sorry, so sorry I should have been looking'. She thought our car was proceeding onto the roundabout and just drove into our stationery car and of course she was going far too fast.

With details exchanged, the car was just about driveable and we decided to finish the journey to work and seek medical advice there. Once the paramedics at the airport saw the damage they said there was no alternative but to take me to the local hospital for an X-ray. An airport car was summonsed and Jez and I were taken to hospital.

On arrival at the hospital, my head was strapped to a board so I could not move and I was so scared I was going to be sick and choke on it, as it was so busy in A & E. I was left in the corridor which seemed to be for an endless amount of time waiting to go to X-ray and I was so cold that my feet were numb.

I was delighted to see a friendly face, it was Jez whose injuries were not too severe. Unfortunately I had a severe whiplash and would be off work for the next three months. How could this have happened just as I received the news I had been promoted to A4. At least the house had now been transferred into my name but now I was going to be out of action and if the cabin crew recruitment came up I would not pass the medical.

The damage to my neck and back proved to be a lot more serious than originally diagnosed, as both were completely out of alignment and it was not going to be an easy task to put this right. The physiotherapist explained that this was going to be a lengthy procedure and might result in surgery. The injury to my neck had resulted in severe migraines every two to three weeks and these were in fact more debilitating than the back injury.

I was unable to move my head from right to left so driving was extremely dangerous and even worse the migraines caused such terrible sickness I would have to stop several times on the way to work.

After a visit to the Neurologist, I was advised that the damage to my head and neck were causing the migraines and I would need medication to improve the pain. There was no way with the amount of damage that I would be able to pass a medical and be fit enough to fly for the foreseeable future. I was absolutely devastated.

Despite various types of medication, the headaches still continued. The solicitor handling the compensation case told me that until I had reached the point where this was the best it was going to be, the case would not be settled. Therefore the doctors would have to decide how much of the damage would be permanent.

Unbelievably, to stand any chance of getting back to fitness, I had to pay for the physio treatment and consultants fees as even an interim payment did not seem to be forthcoming. The accident was not my fault as I was merely a passenger. Not only was I having to endure all this pain but I had to put all these costs on my credit card. It seemed never ending, would I ever be fit again?

The part that I could not come to terms with was that the person who inflicted all this pain and damage had restarted her flying career, there would be no case to answer as she hit the car from behind and had pleaded guilty. However, this did not make it any easier for me, I wanted to face her in court and tell her how angry I felt that she was flying and she had taken the chance of me doing the same, maybe forever, in one careless moment.

There were so many trips to different doctors for insurance assessments and I hated the way I was cross-examined about whether I had any symptoms beforehand. Even to the point when I had my first baby and had suffered headaches from medication that I had been prescribed, I felt I was the one on trial.

The Solicitors advised that the case would probably take five years and I knew at this point I would need clearance from the airline medical centre to return to work as very soon my wages would be reduced. I just needed to convince them that I could resume work and get back to some normality otherwise the bitterness would get the better of me.

CHAPTER 15

I had three teenagers at home, as I had taken on responsibility for my daughter's best friend, Alex, whose Mother had suffered an accident. It became clear when we visited Alex's mother in the hospital that it was going to take some time for the injuries to repair, as she had suffered a broken arm and hand. There was no way that Alex could look after herself as she was only 12, so we agreed that in the short term, she would move into our house as she already went to school with my children and it seemed the ideal solution for the time being.

Alex stayed with us, sharing a bedroom with my daughter Elizabeth. They grew to be like sisters and she became part of our family and spending a lot of time between her mother and ourselves. All three children would argue, fight and row like most brothers and sisters but once they were old enough to go out clubbing and partying, they were extremely protective of one another and would look out for each other. They knew they had better all come home together, otherwise there would be trouble if out late at night.

The divorce was not going well and was becoming more and more acrimonious and I needed to keep the house at all costs as more disruption to the children was unacceptable.

I became more and more terrified of the post arriving every day. It always seemed to hold bad news such as outstanding debts that I was totally unaware of but somehow suspiciously seemed to bear my name.

The migraines were intolerable and I was able to sympathise with people who had always suffered with them, these were no ordinary headaches. It was one morning whilst on my way to work, having stopped already to be sick, my vision became blurred & the pain was unbearable. This could be so easy, no more solicitors or doctors, no more debt and bad news. I was driving down the straight stretch of road going faster and faster, it was the early hours of the morning so there was no one else on the road whom I could hurt, the speedometer was showing 60, 70 suddenly 90 in a few moments it would soon be all over.

Suddenly I saw a deer with its young at the side of the road which somehow brought me back to my senses, how could I do this to my children, they would never forgive me. I was just being selfish to leave them at this vital stage in their lives, how cruel and thoughtless I was being. Perhaps I would just continue driving and not stop until the diesel ran out and disappear like my ex-husband had done and leave all the mess for someone else to pick up.

I had to accept that flying would be out of the question, I was getting older and now my health had deteriorated both mentally and physically, I might need surgery but why was I being so pathetic? This was very unlike me. I had to either give in or be strong, something that my father had always been in the past, I had to get a grip, there were loads of people who were a lot worse off than I was. Maybe this was the turning point but I knew I had to make it happen if I wanted life to change. It was no good just hoping it would all go away I had to help myself but had I the strength to do this?

I stood in Court before a very irritated Judge - this was costing me huge amounts of money to wait with my very expensive paid by the hour London Barrister. Eventually, the Judge was not prepared to waste any more of the court's valuable time waiting for the other parties to arrive. I held my breath as His Honour made an order for me to keep the house on payment of the agreed sum to my ex-husband but I had to agree to settle his outstanding debts which he had managed to levy on the property.

In usual circumstances, I would have gone into a very low place but this was music to my ears, I had at last actually managed to achieve something positive, even though it was going to cost me more money. I was not sure how I was ever going to pay this back but now I could perhaps at long last move on. Maybe, just maybe, I could work on my fitness and when recruitment opened, I would be more determined than ever I would be ready.

No more wallowing in self-pity, I needed to join a gym. I had been told by the neurologist that there was a very strong painkiller that if taken at the onset of a migraine, would stop the sickness and maybe make the migraines more bearable. This was a lifeline and if nothing else a crutch to help me cope whilst I received other treatments.

When I arrived home and saw my children I realised I had made the right decision, what came over me I thought, people had a lot worse circumstances than I had. With the ongoing treatment on my neck and back and the tablets which seemed to be helping curb the sickness, it was 'onwards' and 'upwards'. How could I possibly have even considered leaving all these problems and debt to my teenage children; after all, it was not their fault and they needed to continue with their studies and not worry about what was happening at home.

At this rate I was going to be one of the oldest cabin crew on record, would I even be able to undertake the arduous six week training course. Fitness was imperative and I still had the terrifying problem of being able to learn to swim. I did not even like the water much and it had become a stand up joke with family and friends that I never actually got my hair wet when I went in the water. Friends would comment on the fact I went to aqua classes and came out of the water with dry hair. I didn't even like being splashed!! Wet hair to me was a sign of deep water and drowning.

This was of course no good as one of the criteria for cabin crew was being able to swim a length of the pool and being able to pull yourself up a rope ladder into a large rubber inflatable dingy. At the moment I was not even be able to swim, let alone a length. As for pulling myself up a ladder with a lifejacket on into a dingy, impossibilities take me a bit longer to get to grips with!

People used to tell me I would soon get in the boat with sharks swimming around me. Believe you me, you have not seen the sheer panic if I was unable to put my foot on the bottom or got my hair wet - I do not think so - I would have drowned before this happened. In fact, the sharks were the least of my worries as the water would get me first, I would not even be able to jump from the aircraft.

The very thought of being able to help people from an aircraft to a life raft seemed impossible, I would need help from the passengers myself! I was being really pathetic when I see all these children swimming, so I decided I needed to have swimming lessons, preferably on my own and in the dark so no one could see how bad and scared I really was.

I arrived at the pool where the area was sectioned off and found five ladies and four men who were also non-swimmers on the poolside; everyone was about the same age as myself and just as scared. We were given armbands and a rubber ring to put on, much to everyone's amusement. I did not care, in fact, I hardly thought this was enough, where was the life jacket? I suppose it was only four feet of water, I could stand up if I wanted to and put my foot on the bottom, which I did regularly!

The swimming instructor arrived and to my absolute horror I actually knew him as he was a teacher from my children's primary school - how embarrassing was this going to be. 'Hey Ho', I was there now. We all stepped into the water and told to swim across to the other side of the pool, if we felt we could, with feet off the bottom. This was pretty disastrous, there was plenty of splashing and not much movement to the other side.

Ugh, I actually got my hair wet, even worse the swimming instructor asked if I could just let go of his hand, which had gone white as I was squeezing it so hard.

I went twice a week for six weeks and gradually the air was let down in my armbands and I was left with just the rubber ring. Somehow, and I am not sure how, I managed with some of the others to swim the length of the pool unaided. When I realised I was in the 6ft end I almost started to panic but the end was near now. All we had to do was swim the whole length of the pool unaided to obtain a certificate.

Halfway down the pool, I felt I was going to have a heart attack as I found breaststroke so tiring but I was so near the end I could not give up now. Mission complete I could now swim breaststroke unaided at the age of forty something! The swimming instructor advised us to stay in the shallows for the time being until we became more confident, especially in the sea! See, I thought to myself, you are never too old to learn something new.

At long last, my divorce was finalised, I had kept a roof over our heads and my finances were extremely bad but not insurmountable. I was working as an A4 for one of the most well known airlines in the world and I could at least swim. Maybe not as a Channel swimmer but I would be able to get by, hopefully.

Perhaps, just perhaps, I could make the dream come true next time recruitment for cabin crew came up. If I was not too old by then (American Airlines take on cabin crew in their 80s I understand) there was hope for me, if I still had the strength to push a trolley and open an aircraft door.

I recalled how I overheard one of the younger girls, in a previous job, saying to her friends "Titsy Sue thinks she is going to fly, she'll be lucky at her age, it's for young people." Well, I am not very well endowed, so wrong on first part and "Oh well" nothing ventured nothing gained and you know what they say about people who eavesdrop, so we will see. It is amazing how many put downs and let downs I had had to endure, especially the older I became because it still hurts whatever age you are, maybe it made me more determined to succeed.

Surely nothing could stop me now?

CHAPTER 16

Maybe I was at a better place in my life now and hopefully, things might improve now that I had the house. I would probably be working until well past retirement but I would live for today, even next week seemed too far away. My health had started to improve and I thought with a couple of tweaks I might be able to pass the medical I would be required to take for cabin crew as my neck and back seemed to be stronger.

I was at work one day when a work colleague showed me an article in the company newsletter. To my delight, they were recruiting for cabin crew and there, at last, were the application details. I felt the advantage of working on the ground would now be of great benefit to this interview as I had so much more knowledge of the company itself and the whole workings of the airline industry. I could at least give it my best shot. I therefore filled in my application form with excitement and was thrilled when they called me for an interview.

The interview day arrived and it was amazing how much easier it felt to be a part of the company already as the questions I would be required to answer would be mostly about the workings of the airline business. Especially the Premium passengers as most of the revenue from business card holders support the remainder of the aircraft. It was vital to know exactly how much of the revenue was brought into the company by big organisations whose employees travelled with us on a regular basis, knowing the different card tiers and which lounges they were allowed in would hold me in good stead. This aspect was vital to most card holders, as passengers were always desperate to climb to the top tier to enable them to gain access to the top lounges and be able to always have access to their favourite seat on the aircraft.

Access to seat 1A for instance on the aircraft was vitally important for some passengers, who felt that no one else should be allowed to sit in this seat. If it had already been taken, they wanted the person to move, many coming unstuck when it was the other passenger's favourite seat too!

All I had to do now was keep my head, keep my concentration alert as very often the three interviewers would be sitting in front of a large window; with the aircraft going backwards and forwards, this could be very distracting. I was told to keep my wits about me and not to get sidetracked watching a 777 waiting to take its position on the tarmac ready for take off. One person would ask a section of the questions whilst the other two watched and then the next one would join in or take over. I must not get flustered if I was not sure of an answer.

My uniform and personal appearance were immaculate so all I could do now was give it my best as I knew there would not be many more chances for me to re-apply if this failed. Of course, my fitness would be called into questioning but I was able to assure them that I was up to the job and I would be able to pass any medical. I would take painkillers if I had to.

There were so many scenarios to deal with "What would you do if a passenger started shouting and verbally abusing you, how would you try and calm the situation?," "If a card holder on a certain tier thought they were entitled to higher lounge access and arrived on board still feeling angry and aggrieved how would you deal with this to make sure you were not going to have to spend the next 8 hours crossing the 'pond' with them still annoyed?, "How would you deal with passengers who were scared of flying?," the list went on and on. Luckily I had been dealing with all these problems as ground crew and was able to give factual answers as most of these things were a common occurrence.

After about an hour I knew I was beginning to flag and it was extremely difficult not to become distracted by the passing aircraft. At last having checked all about how my family felt about my flying and my being able to explain that the three children were virtually grown up now, the interview came to an end. I had done all I could so I smiled and left the room. I kept going over and over the interview in my mind thinking how I could have answered the questions better, but it was over, all I could do was wait and hope.

My work colleague who had also applied, felt the same and we compared notes - why did I answer that question that way and the interviewers seemed to be making a huge amount of notes. Luckily the group scenario we had to take part in went a lot better this time and as the compulsory foreign test had been removed it was now just a waiting game.

In September 2004 at the age of 50 something, the letter I had awaited for, what seemed most of my adult life, arrived. I was so scared to open it as failure again, I knew this time, would be hard to take. For a while I just sat looking at the envelope and feeling afraid of how awful I was going to feel, especially if my work colleague had been successful and I had not. This would be hard to stomach. How was I going to feel congratulating her when deep down I was so sad. Well, the only way of finding out was to open the envelope. In a few seconds all would be revealed.

It was coffee time and my children had started to come down in search of food and they wondered what on earth I was doing drinking a coffee and looking at an envelope propped up on the table. "Open the envelope" they said excitedly but it never seems quite that simple as you get older. I suppose I was very lucky that I still had my job at the airport, this could be just a setback but the years were passing very quickly now I thought.

I could not believe my eyes, I just kept going over and over the words in the letter "We are very pleased to confirm that you have been successful in your application for cabin crew." The rest of the letter all blurred into one. From then on the excitement in the kitchen was electric and even brought my son down from his slumbers wondering what all the noise was about.

I was in a complete daze from then on, I was finally going to become cabin crew for one of the most prestigious airline companies in the world. It was just unbelievable and I could not wait to contact my friend to see if she too had been successful as I would be very sad if she had not. I hoped she had as selfishly it would mean we would be able to share accommodation when undertaking the training.

I had not felt such excitement for such a long time and it was really difficult to explain just how I felt. To some, this was just another job, but to me at my age and after such a lot of adversities in my life, I had finally achieved my dream.....well nearly. I had almost forgotten the long six week training course ahead.

CHAPTER 17

All I had to do now, I say all, after such a long wait was to visit my optician as the neurologist had confirmed that it would now be possible for me to return to wearing contact lenses. He understood the type of job I would be doing so it might be more helpful to now have new glasses or contact lenses, as the job would require reading from a card with instructions in poor light, say at night.

I therefore went ahead and made a routine eye examination, never thinking there would be any more than a large bill for the contact lenses and new glasses. Little did I know what was to happen that would rock my world once again.

The optician had not been looking at my eyes for very long before he sat back in his chair with a concerned look on his face. It's amazing that look that sends an uneasy feeling and makes you realise that all is not well. Surely there was nothing wrong with my eyes, I had no problems apart from being short sighted which most people can suffer from. Suddenly he was saying the words "I would like my colleague to have a look at your left eye."

All I could think of was more expense. The optician had seen something that he was not happy with in my left eye and wanted me to see his colleague to confirm his suspicions. He was making an appointment for me to see him immediately. What was the problem and how serious is this that I had to go so quickly? He was very kind and did not want to alarm me; always makes me laugh when the medical profession make these statements, the look on their faces usually says it all followed by "I am sure it is nothing to worry about."

I left the opticians with no contact lenses or glasses but an appointment to see a more senior ophthalmologist the very next day.

I spent the next few hours examining my eyes to see if I could see anything amiss. By this time I had worked myself up into a complete state of whether I was losing my eyesight or had a brain tumour. Why did this have to happen now just as I was about to start my training course, typical, and I was worried about my headaches and back.

JP took me to the appointment and I was absolutely stunned as I heard the words coming out of the ophthalmologist's mouth. After a thorough examination, this lovely man was telling me, I had a shadow on my left eye which needed to be looked at more closely. He would speak to his colleague at Moorfields, who had actually trained him and would see if he could see me as soon as possible.

So a trip to Harley Street it was and I was to meet yet again one of the kindest & nicest men I have ever met in my life, Mr Ford, who together with his lovely secretary, were to look after me and my eye.

After a lot of tests and drops in my eyes, which made me look even more like someone out of a horror movie, he gave me the news I suppose I had been dreading. There was no easy way of putting this but he had found a tumour in my left eye and an operation would have to be undertaken as soon as possible to find out whether it was benign or malignant. I could hear the words coming out of his mouth but I could not quite believe what I was hearing. I did sometimes see a dark shadow when the sun shone in my eye but I took no notice as it did not affect my eyesight.

I explained how I had been wanting to fly as cabin crew for what seemed like forever and now I had actually been offered the job this was to happen. Mr. Ford told me not to worry, he had everything in hand and he would carry out the operation himself the following week. He would then have a clear indication as to how we would be able to progress with the upcoming training. I wanted to ask the question but was half afraid of the answer I would get. Still I had to know "Was I going to lose my eye, or even worse " Was I going to go blind."

Until the operation whereby a biopsy would be undertaken, it was difficult to ascertain the outcome but I somehow knew I was in the best possible hands and I realised that my life and sight were far more important than any job.

I was now on my way to Moorfields in London, which I knew to be the top Eye Hospital in the world, with JP and my overnight bag which I was told to bring just in case. Very ominous I thought. Everyone at the hospital was extremely kind and supportive, I was very nervous as I was prepared for theatre. I wondered if I would wake up with only one eye. Ever since I received the news I kept closing my left eye and trying to visualise just what it would be like, especially when driving. It's very strange the feelings you suddenly have as we take our sight totally for granted, we wake up each day and open our eyes and just expect to be able to see, likewise being able to hear.

JP tried to reassure me that whatever the results it would all be alright as he wheeled me down to the operating theatre. I had this terrible sense of doom and strange thoughts of never being able to see my children married, or seeing any grandchildren. What am I like, I was treating this as though it was the worse case scenario. It might be good news, fingers crossed.

I suppose I did not realise as I said goodbye to JP just how nervous I really was. Maybe it was the pre-med as I remember asking the medical team whether I had been given the anesthetic and if I opened my eyes would I be able to see everything like the lights and equipment. Even worse, my cheek at close quarters when they take the eye out of its socket, yuck!!

The staff found this hilarious and were all laughing as well as Mr Ford who entered the operating theatre. He would remind me of this throughout my future visits to him and would say "how is your cheek doing these days."

When I woke up, having seen nothing at all during the operation, I was covered in bandages over my left eye and all I could see was JP sitting asleep by my bed with a beautiful black and gold Halloween bear next to me he had been out and bought. Well, at least I could see out of my right eye which was a result. I was terrified of opening my other eye but I would not have been able to see anyway as there seemed to be something in the way, which I later found out was a radiotherapy disk.

JP woke up as Mr. Ford entered the room to deliver the verdict. The bandages were removed and I gingerly opened my eye to find I could see, albeit rather hazily, but then the disk had to be removed, what was that all about? The biopsy had come back and the tumour was inconclusive, neither benign nor malignant, which was such a relief and I would need to have a regular six month check up to keep a check on it. Unfortunately, one way or another it could not be removed without taking my sight so it was best left well alone for the immediate future. " Would the tumour suddenly turn malignant" I found myself asking. Unfortunately, there was no answer to this question at this point.

Amazingly I found I had such faith in Mr. Ford's opinion and I knew that he would look after me whatever happened in the future which helped me so much in coming to terms with this sudden unexpected news. The next question was how was I going to proceed with my airline training course that I was to undergo in a matter of a few weeks. Mr. Ford told me to carry on as normal, as to all intents and purpose if I had not gone for new contact lenses I would have never known about the tumour. Therefore, he would confirm that I was "fit to fly" as I was no different now than I was at the interview.

It is strange how once you know you have something wrong healthwise you do feel different, I seemed to be able to see the black shadow more frequently now and it definitely did not like bright lights or sunlight but I must not let this alter my plans as I had been lucky with the diagnosis at this stage.

Travelling on the tube was extremely difficult with my eye all covered in bandages and I understand now how frightening it can be when your vision is impaired. Without JP to hold onto, people just pushed past me and I nearly fell down the stairs leading to the underground. Even with the bandages being fully visible, people were unbelievably uncaring and this was not even rush hour. This whole procedure of getting home on both the underground and mainline trains made me suddenly far more aware of how people with visual impairment, or in fact any other disabilities, have to cope as people are so rude and thoughtless.

I was delighted JP had been with me and was pleased to arrive home safely, as by this time I had a splitting headache but at least I would be recovered enough to attend the course without my 'Pudsey Bear' bandage so no one would be any the wiser - hopefully.

Of course the whole procedure had cost £2,500, money of which I did not have and it would have to be paid from my ever increasing credit card but I was hopeful that eventually I would receive a pay out from the accident. However, as my father had pointed out to me, what cost can you put on your health and I was lucky that the tumour was not malignant at this stage and not spread.

CHAPTER 18

When I finally read the letter, it stated I would be given a final date when I could be released from my A4 ground duties and a start date for my cabin crew course. I would of course have to pass all aspects of the training to obtain my wings. Having left I did not know if I would be allowed to just return to my old ground staff employment, or find out whether I would be based in Gatwick or Heathrow until the course had been successfully completed. I hoped my home base would be Gatwick, but I knew I could not be fussy. I just now needed to concentrate on the training as there was not an easy path back, if any. However, I had been in this position before so I knew I could do it. A month later, the starting date arrived at long last and I was off and running. Or so I thought.

Luckily my friend Claire and I managed to book into a local hotel up near Heathrow and this is where we would stay for the next six weeks, although we did manage a couple of days home during this time. The room, I remembered, was quite small and very drab but it was cheap as we had to fund this ourselves so we were lucky to get subsidised canteen food whilst at the training centre. We were only paid a very minimal wage so we learned to be quite frugal, although there was so much work to do that we did not have any time to socialise or barely eat.

Every day would find us back in our small room revising or getting ready for the next days exhausting activities. I was not sure how I was ever going to remember all the different parts of the aircraft as the Safety Equipment and Procedures training, (from now on shortened to SEP training) had to be undertaken every year to keep our Flying licence in check, was very daunting and it seemed the dread of most cabin crew, no matter how long they had been flying.

On reaching the classroom in the Hangar for our fifth day of training, I was asked to go to the office as they had received my medical records and they were not happy with the contents. What could be the problem now?

I could tell when I entered the office that the doctor was not happy and it now seemed that I was to be taken off the training course as they were very concerned about my eye. How could this be? The specialist had written a very detailed account of the situation with my eye and the letter quite clearly said that I was "Fit to Fly." This team thought otherwise, even though I was under the supervision of one of the top Eye Specialists the Airline medical doctors decided to override this decision.

I was just beginning to settle into the course, make friends, and had taken the hotel accommodation with Claire for six weeks, as we had decided failure was not in our remit and now I was being taken off the course whilst this problem of my eye was being dealt with. Goodness knows how long it would be before another course came along and horror of horrors I now had no job to go back to, does this never end.

I rang the Eye Specialist and of course, he was in the operating theatre so would get back to me later that day. The wait seemed endless and meanwhile, the trainers and other trainees were absolutely mortified that after nearly a week into the training I was not going to be able to stay on the course, I was gutted.

After what seemed like hours, the Specialist returned my call and obviously he was fully aware of all my circumstances in respect of my eye and the job I was undertaking. He had been so very kind to me and told me that he would have no problem in writing the letter stating that the Airlines would require to verify my competence to fly. He was extremely annoyed at being questioned because he was the top Specialist in his field and this was a direct attack on his ability to give his expert opinion and he did not like being questioned in this way.

I overheard the conversation that went between the Specialist and the Airline Health Authorities and it was quite evident that he was far from amused at having his many years of experience in the top Eye Hospital in London brought into question. I was delighted to return to my colleagues bright and early next morning and the trainers would catch up the previous day's training with me later on.

We were having difficulty just with the initial training. There was just so much more to the job than, as most people put it, being a 'glorified waitress'. Believe me, you would not say that when you are waiting your turn to launch yourself down the 737, 777 and 747 escape chutes.

The noise in the hangar of the escape slides being released was absolutely deafening and even more so when we donned overalls and were told just follow the line and jump down the chute with our arms crossed in front of us.

The 737 slide was not too high so was not too bad but the 777 and 747 are suddenly a different ball game and all would have been alright if the person in front of me had not decided at the last minute to suddenly stop and was too afraid to jump. That hesitation meant there was time to think about what we were just about to do and the height involved but we were told we had to jump otherwise it would be a failure. Well here goes, I just closed my eyes and leapt, leaving the other poor girl in floods of tears and fearing not ever being able to complete this task.

Luckily the above element and leaving the aircraft when landing on water and getting everyone off the aircraft onto the life raft only had to be done in initial training, thank God. I always prayed if ever the aircraft did go down, please do not let it be on water, as I would not fancy my, or the passengers chances!!

The noise in the Hangar was immense because there were so many trainees taking part in training on the different types of aircraft. Certain words would remain in my memory for the rest of my life 'Brace Brace', 'Wait, Wait slide inflating' and 'Jump Jump' being just a few of them. Everyone was at a different point in the exercise so it was always confusing as to what I should be shouting but I knew I had to get it absolutely correct.

We were always split into groups and no one ever wanted to go first, especially as we were not sure what was going to be asked of us. Sometimes it was better to go first and get it over with, or watch someone go first and learn by their mistakes.

The doors were extremely heavy on the 737 as they were not power-assisted and I wondered how I was going to find the strength to open the door, mind you if a fire was behind me I knew I would be able to find the strength from somewhere, it is surprising what you can do in an emergency. The girt bar was a metal bar that was attached to the bustle, which housed the escape slide in the door. This had to be engaged when the doors were cross-checked so the evacuation slide could be deployed in an emergency.

Every time I went on board an aircraft to go on holiday, I used to wonder what the crew were actually doing and how serious a mistake this would be for everyone if this procedure was not carried out at the beginning and end of each flight.

The call would be made by the Senior, in those days the Cabin Manager, 'Cabin Crew Doors to Automatic and cross check', which I soon realised meant arming the door once the aircraft moves back from the jetty on its own power, so that if an evacuation was needed the door could be opened and the slide would inflate allowing passengers to leave the aircraft safely. Failure to put the aircraft in the correct position would mean the door would be opened and with no slide and passengers would just fall out from a height, resulting in serious injury and in most cases death.

Likewise, on landing, the call would be once again made 'Cabin Crew door to Manual and Cross Check' as when the aircraft comes onto the jetty we were made fully aware that if the slide inflated when the door has opened, the person on the other side would take the full force of the slide and it would almost certainly be fatal.

Every member of the crew who had the responsibility of a door, was responsible for arming and disarming that door and having put the door in the correct mode would then cross-check with the person on the opposite door, just as a fail-safe to make sure this procedure had been done properly to avoid an accident. This whole procedure would then be confirmed to the person in charge at the front so it could be recorded.

How was I going to remember all of this on a busy aircraft, I was glad my opposite number would be checking me as I soon realised the importance of this procedure. Then I would, by now, need to be wearing my flat shoes again so as my high heeled shoes would not tear the slide, making sure all the passengers screens were out, enabling them to see the safety demonstration and preparing to carry out this procedure in time with the instructions being given on the prerecorded tape.

The cabin crew always made this procedure look so easy and effortless and of course, over the years, I realised how many times this had been undertaken, it was just done like clockwork but not to ever be complacent.

The first part was easy opening the little blue bag which contained, hopefully, all the equipment you would need. However, if the person who had used it before had failed to replace an item, you would be standing out there with hundreds of faces all looking at you. Note to self, always check contents of bag when laying equipment out ready for demo so as not to look ill prepared.

The card with all the instructions was the easy part as it was just shown to the passengers, then the exits would be pointed out, 'There are two exits at the rear of the aircraft, two in the centre and two at the front of the aircraft', simple as long as you remembered exactly where you were standing as this could differ with each flight. Some of my friends still 'pull my leg' when they talk about my job and say 'The exits are here, here and here," pointing these out with their hands and arms!

Next part 'If the cabin air supply fails, masks like these (pull dummy mask out of the bag and hold up to the passengers) will appear automatically, stay in your seat and pull a mask towards you, this will open your oxygen supply, place the mask over your mouth and nose, like this, and breathe normally, adjusting the band to secure it, do make sure your own mask is fitted before helping anyone else'. Not too bad as the elastic did not need to go right over the head. Mask back in bag, hopefully I am in time with the recorded message, as now came the tricky part.

Holding the brightly coloured yellow lifejacket above your head, then at the right part of the reading, passing this over your immaculate hairdo and pulling it over your head. Not easy I found with my hair in a bun or a french pleat but then nor was the putting the tapes around your waist and crossing them over your back and making a double bow around your waist. Luckily, there was always a slight pause, both on the recording and if being read manually, to enable crew to catch up as obviously this procedure takes time to complete correctly. If the double bow could be pulled undone in the test by the examiner, it would result in a failure, as in an emergency the lifejacket might come undone.

Passengers would be watching all this and I soon realised you could end up very red faced if you made a mistake, when we were practicing there was always lots of laughter from the others and trainers as we fought with the tapes. Thank goodness we walked through the cabin still wearing the lifejacket whilst securing the passengers ready for take off and removed in the privacy of the galley so that our hair could be readjusted as it very often looked like 'Worzel'.

Securing the passengers in their seats was vital to their safety and until this procedure was undertaken, the 'cabin secure' could not be given in by the senior to the flight crew. This meant making sure everyone had their seatbelts fastened, the seats were in the upright position, no handbags on laps, which often proved to be extremely difficult as some passengers would not be parted from their handbags as they did not want them to go under the seat in front of them, or in the overhead locker. It was explained if the aircraft had to be evacuated quickly, there would be no time to pick up hand luggage and you would not want to be tripping over someone's handbag straps, as it may be the lights would go out and this procedure could have to be undertaken in darkness.

It was explained how many passengers in an emergency stop the flow of passengers going to the exits by trying to open the overhead lockers to retrieve their hand luggage so that they can take this down the slide with them, which could result in slowing the evacuation process down and result in loss of life. A very stark reminder to us all.

However, on a lighter note, would I ever be good enough at this to be able to show my professional face out in front of passengers without them thinking it was part of a comedy act, as this morning I managed to put the lifejacket on inside out, the give away was the writing on the front saying this side facing the body. The easiest part was pulling the toggle to pretend to inflate, blowing in the red tube to increase the air and there was a light and a whistle for attracting attention. Believe me, there would be plenty of whistle blowing if I was to fall into any water.

I soon realised there was so much more to the job than I had ever thought as there were serious consequences in not follow procedures, hence the rigorous training. When I hear people saying "Oh it's just being a glorified waitress"; well I can tell you there is so much more to the job, as I am about to explain, come with me for just a few hours.

Cabin crew are there basically for passengers safety.

The different doors on the aircraft and how these were opened was just one aspect, this was all bearing in mind that it was just boarding the aircraft in normal circumstances which 9 times out of 10 it would be but we had to be trained in how this would all pan out if an emergency occurred. Even going on board the 'mock up' aircraft was challenging, although what am I talking about, every aspect seemed challenging. We were called forward in pairs and having put the aircraft doors into the correct mode we were then told to take our seats and prepare for an emergency landing.

It seemed so strange that I was not afraid of the aircraft going down but just getting all the instructions in the right order after the alarm was raised by the Captain "This is an emergency Brace Brace." We then had to have our hands and feet in the correct position whilst shouting to the passengers "Brace Brace" and when the aircraft had come to its final stop it was then that everything seems to happen with such precision and it was up to cabin crew to get this correct.

Shutting the alarm off first, always a good idea as it was deafening, looking outside for hazards such as water or fire, as you would not want to direct passengers directly into a hazard, making sure the door was in the correct mode, then opening the door whilst shouting at the passengers to unfasten their seatbelts, not taking anything with them and come this way. Holding onto the grab handles on each side of the aircraft door was vital, whilst shouting "wait wait slide inflating," as passengers in their panic might inadvertently push you out before the slide had fully inflated and then waiting for the slide to inflate before telling passengers to "Jump Jump."

This whole procedure took a matter of minutes but to make sure it was all in the correct order seemed to take forever but speed of course was of the essence to make sure that all the passengers were off the aircraft and safely down the slide, checking the aircraft before leaving yourself. It had to all work like clockwork and although it was hoped that this action would never be needed, all cabin crew had to pass this test and I could see why. The safety of the passengers was in our hands.

CHAPTER 19

Every night we returned to our hotel accommodation and it did not matter what it was like, we were so tired that we were even too tired to eat as there was so much more to learn the next day. On many occasions we would even study overnight. As long as we passed the tests each day, we were another stage nearer to getting our wings.

The next day we were told to bring our clothes for swimming, it was the day I had been dreading and I knew this was going to be make or break. Would I be able to hold my nerve as the water was still very daunting for me. I shared my fears with the others and it appeared I was not the only one to have concerns about the strength we needed to first do the swim and then haul our bodies out of the water into the liferaft.

We went by coach to what appeared to be a local pool where lifeguard training etc took place and there in front of us was this huge up to 35 people capacity liferaft, which was so much bigger than I ever imagined. The instructions were as follows: we had to swim a length of the pool fully clothed complete with a lifejacket, I felt happier about the fact that I would not embarrass myself by drowning. Having swum the length we were required to climb up the rope ladder which hung down the side of this huge black two tiered monster of a liferaft and having reached the top, we had to hurl our bodies over into the craft.

No way was I going to be able to do this without any help which we were told by the trainers they could not do and the best advice they could give us was to try and keep the ladder as close to the raft and not let it come out into the water. More importantly, to try and do this first time as a second attempt would be much harder as our arms would be tired. A second attempt, I would be there all day, as just the thought of climbing up to the top of the raft and pulling myself over the top seemed an impossibility but the thought of falling back and splashing into the water was not on my agenda either.

No one ever really wants to go first, apart from the really good swimmers and the guys with big muscles, but I suppose it was better to get it over and done with as it was not going to get any better. It seemed to reach my turn rather quickly, so did the need to go to the toilet and be sick! Even the lifejacket felt awkward and heavy. I managed to do the swim which seemed miles away from the ladder but as I tentatively put my foot on the bottom run of the ladder, I could feel it moving outwards but as the trainers knew how nervous I was, they had entered the water themselves and were screaming instructions.

The noise of them yelling was ringing in my ears, encouraging me to keep the ladder still and pull my heavyweight body up the never ending treads, I so wanted to let go but was too afraid of falling backwards. I just thought it was better to keep hanging on as the top was in sight, everyone was now shouting and encouraging me to keep going but I could feel my heart pounding and I was sure any minute I was going to have a heart attack. I had reached the top which was all wet and slippery, one last pull and I was over, please do not let me fall back now. I gave one last almighty heave and suddenly I was sliding like some seal across a huge expanse of plastic which was the bottom of the raft.

I was not sure whether I was still alive as my arms and chest were absolutely exhausted but to my surprise, everyone including the trainers were cheering - I had overcome my greatest fear and was thrilled I had done it.

If you have never been afraid of water or anything else that makes you freeze with fear, you could not possibly understand what a big deal this had been for me and what it had taken to overcome this. Yes, I would never be a brilliant Olympic swimmer but I could at least hold my own, or maybe have the confidence now to save someone from drowning, but I know that if we landed on water and the door was above the waterline, I would have it open and be getting the passengers out, as I am sure the adrenalin would kick in.

Even just writing about this brings back memories of the camaraderie on that day and I still feel myself filling up with emotion. I could not have done this without everyones help and support. I will be forever grateful to all those who made this possible.

CHAPTER 20

We decided we would give homework a rest for just one night and meet up for a drink as there were a few of us staying in the same hotel and at this point we were all halfway through the training.

The next morning it was back on target with Medical training. Firstly was being able to locate where all the medical equipment was stowed so as in an emergency we would not be hunting around and wasting valuable time which could save someone's life. Then of course, having found the equipment, we had to be able to put the different pieces together and be able to use them. One of the most serious medical emergencies on board an aircraft is a suspected heart attack where resuscitation equipment has to be used.

We were taught how to recognise the symptoms of the different medical emergencies that could occur whilst you were over a vast amount of sea and not able to land immediately. This was invaluable information due to passengers being sometimes completely unaware of the physical changes that occur in the body when they are flying, especially if they have medical problems already which can be exacerbated due to the pressure on board, or stress at just going to the airport.

This information regarding the defibrillator and being able to carry out CPR, especially on board where normally the space is limited, was invaluable as although you always hope never to have to use it, someone's life might depend on being able to carry this procedure out correctly. Even if not successful, at least it gives the person a fighting chance of getting the heart pumping again rather than just standing by helplessly and I am all for everyone being taught this from school children upwards.

Choking, asthma attacks, strokes, childbirth, etc were all covered under this part of the training and of course, a final exam both practical and theory had to be passed and retaken each year to keep up-to-date with any changes.

Little did I know that I would later in life have some of this training put to the test and one of the most wonderful and yet difficult experiences of my entire life was being present when Elizabeth, my daughter, was in labour. Seeing my own daughter go through giving birth in virtually the same way as myself was the only time when I wished I could have done it for her but the end result was our beautiful grandson and the bond we share is a truly wonderful gift that cannot be compared, apart from giving birth myself. I only hoped I would not need to put all this information into practise on board an aircraft. At least I had actually seen the umbilical cord cut, which I always found rather daunting.

I felt all fingers and thumbs being watched very closely by the medical examiners, making sure I put the different parts of the equipment together correctly so they worked during the practical examination and remembering to put the patches on Annie (the plastic dummy used for training) correctly and turn the defib on otherwise no commands would be issued. Always a bit of a giveaway when silence prevails and nothing is happening.

It was such a relief to see Annie's chest rising as not getting the two rescue breaths in would result in failure. Likewise, not locking the arms out during the 30 compressions and at the correct depth on the chest at the right rhythm would also result in failure. However, it was extremely tiring on the arms as the machine never gave you the command that the person was breathing again and you could stop, we had to wait to be told by the examiner. Practical medical over, just the theory to do now so more homework for us tonight and no more getting together for a quick drink. Clear heads were needed.

The fire training was a lot of the trainees worst nightmare and I must say although I was not altogether relishing the idea of entering a smoke filled tunnel but having done the water surely this would be easier!! Pulling the smokehood over immaculate hair done in a french pleat or bun was quite difficult and having never done one of these before, it was not a pleasant process. Inside of the smokehood smelt of smoke and of course, because these were training hoods, there was no oxygen so when they were first put on what with the smell and the feeling of not being able to breath, made this very uncomfortable.

I found the secret was to pull it over my head, ignore the burning smell, tie the tapes and then breath gently because if you started to breath more rapidly, panic sets in. Several of the other trainees did not like this procedure and did not want to wear the smokehoods let alone go into the smoke filled chamber. I felt really sorry for some of the others and tried to keep them from over-breathing but panic can then set off claustrophobia and like all parts of the training this was a very vital part and had to be undertaken successfully.

Once the smokehoods were on we were told to enter the smoke filled aircraft chamber and we each had to find three lighted items located somewhere in the cabin before we could leave the chamber. Once in the room, the smoke seemed really dense and at first, it was difficult to focus but I just followed the person in front of me and just hoped I could find the lights quickly and get out. It was lovely to take the stinking smokehoods off and it certainly did nothing for your hair although that would probably be the last thing on your mind in a real fire.

Claire and I were just discussing how glad we were that the smoke training was over when we were split into two groups and entered into a room that had aircraft seats in it. We were told one group would be passengers and the others cabin crew who would be walking through the cabin. Suddenly we would discover a fire and be expected to have one person locate the source of the fire, the next collect the relevant equipment whilst the third member went on the intercom to the flight crew to tell them about the fire.

This meant donning the smokehoods again and dispensing a BCF, which lasted 15 seconds, into the fire to put it out - I had not realised I would need to have firefighting skills as well but I soon understood if not located quickly just how a fire could soon get out of hand and on board an aircraft there was very little time as the Captain would then be looking for somewhere to land. It must have been even worse when smoking was allowed on board and how passengers used to put cigarettes out in the toilet bins, hence fires could easily start.

Hence the last part of the fire training was putting on fire gloves and discharging a BCF cylinder into an oven that had caught alight. I could see how quickly the fire could spread if went undetected so obviously although this was not very pleasant it was an extremely important part of the training so that maybe a fire could be arrested before it really got a hold resulting in the aircraft having to make an unscheduled landing.

Claire and I both reeked of smoke when we got back to our room and we could not wait to shower, it was even in our hair and we could smell the indescribable burning smell that lingered in the smokehoods for days. We soon learned that fire training was part of the recurrent yearly dreaded SEP training, that was nice to look forward to but at least we would be prepared next time, for good or bad. We all discussed how we hoped we would never have to encounter a fire when we started actual flying, although one of the trainees said "At least it would be a fresh smokehood and not have that awful smoke aroma." Some consolation we all thought, we would rather not put it to the test.

One thing that would unfortunately be put to the test was how to handle disruptive passengers and I was amazed how often this happened on board. Usually fuelled by alcohol and it did not follow any pattern as to where on the aircraft this might happen, or the type of person we might expect to be having to restrain. Whether it was someone famous or not they would still be treated in the same way and given a formal warning by the Captain if their behaviour was thought to endanger the safety of other passengers, or the aircraft ie. trying to open the doors in mid flight. If the passenger refused to comply it would, in extreme cases, mean restraining action would need to be carried out by members of the crew.

In this regard we were then shown how this restraining would be undertaken and I have to say I was somewhat surprised when we were handed a pair of fingerless gloves, handcuffs and a key. This caused great hilarity amongst a few of the trainees who obviously thought this was not the first time they had handled handcuffs and they knew exactly how they were put on! We had to pair up and I must say I was extremely glad of the wrist protectors as when we backloaded the cuffs and slammed them on each others wrists it was quite painful, this procedure would be most uncomfortable if done on bare wrists. However, if this exercise was actually taking place, the person would not exactly be compliant, they would be kicking, shouting and swearing and in many cases spitting, so their pain would not be uppermost in your thoughts.

Handcuffs on, the next stage was to move passengers away from the offending person and a blanket placed over their head to stop them spitting over everyone and they would need to be restrained in a middle seat by straps that we would need to learn how to apply. The passenger would then be checked on regularly until the aircraft landed and the person would then be escorted off the plane by the police as it is an offence to be drunk on board an aircraft. Likewise the company took a very dim view of this and no matter who you were, or how famous you were, a ban and in some serious cases, a lifetime ban, would be implemented by the company so that they were unable to fly with us again for the time imposed by this ban.

I could think of quite a few people I could use the handcuffs on and throw away the key!

We were taught how to look after ourselves and keep ourselves safe and the above was part of our recurrent SEP training every year, which unfortunately over the years became more and more necessary to implement for some reason. We were told never to board a passenger who was, or we suspected to be, under the influence of alcohol and to stop serving alcohol to passengers who we believed were becoming 'worse for wear', which in itself sometimes proved very controversial as some people handle their drink better than others.

Bad behaviour in many cases was an absolute minefield. I was never surprised at what I might find going on, especially in those very compact and bijou toilets, which are barely big enough for one person let alone two and of course have to be regularly checked for replenishment and security. Still I supposed these passengers are not worried about the cleanliness, or whether there are sufficient toilet rolls and paper towels!

The final exams loomed ever closer as Claire and I sat in our rooms every night going over the different parts of the aircraft, the positions where we would sit and our responsibilities relating to that seat and the equipment stowage. Before each flight, we would be required to attend a briefing where we would meet the Cabin Manager, the Pursers and other crew members. Depending on seniority, we would choose a number relating to the seat on the aircraft where we would be sitting for the whole of the flight.

CHAPTER 21

We soon realised what Briefings, which always took place before each flight, actually meant we would get to meet the other members of the crew, be informed about the flight, who was travelling ie. special needs, children, personalities and whether Special Services would be attending, the list was endless.

Even more worrying, we would be asked either individual questions which could be about anything on the aircraft, such as a piece of equipment, or go around the room with each cabin crew member taking part in a scenario on board. Each cabin crew member would then be asked a medical question and depending on the person in charge on the day as to how strictly this would be undertaken. Failure of these questions could lead to being offloaded from the flight. Another person would have to be called from standby to take over and you would be in serious trouble with your Manager.

Some Cabin Managers or Seniors would be more understanding, especially with new crew, as it was extremely daunting to be faced with all the other crew looking at you as the newbie. Others would be out to catch you as having just come out of training you should be well up to speed on all aspects of SEP and therefore be able to answer any questions thrown at us. Most were extremely kind and helpful and remembered back to their first days when they were embarking on their maiden flight.

I soon realised that the more senior you were you could decide where you wanted to work on the aircraft, whether down the back, in Club or in First Class. Even some of the older crew still liked working down the back as it was not as exacting as the other two cabins. If you were really unlucky, you would get the leftover positions that no one wanted such as being in charge in the Galley or doing the duty free, but again you would hope someone would take pity on you and change positions. I could see why it was better to climb up the list as quickly as possible to enable a better choice to be had.

At the moment, the briefings seemed a long way off, just completing the SEP by passing the final exam would help. My brain felt as though it was about to explode but I was so near now and just had to hold my nerve and think of nothing else other than the questions in front of me. The video that precedes the exam went into a complete blur as I was trying so hard to listen to the information as I knew this would be vital when it came to answering the questions, but try as I may, it seemed to go in one ear and out the other. Where was the medical kit found on the 777 and what call would be made in an emergency - I just really wanted to get on with the actual exam now as anything I did not know at this stage was too late now.

Each aircraft had a set of questions, ie the 737, 777 and the 747 together with some general questions. The pass mark was 95% over all but you could not get four questions wrong on one particular aircraft type as the pass mark was based on the whole exam and there was very little margin for error. Combined with this, the exam was timed so I knew I could not spend too long fretting over the questions. I was not sure if I would do all that I could then if there was time left, I could go over these again.

The exam was launched all too quickly, it seemed with a click of a button and I was away. I would answer the different aircraft types in order so as not to muddle the variants up but I could not believe the first question that came up, I was not sure of the answer and panic set in. I was chewing hard on my 'rescue gum' but it did not seem to be helping, I just had to forget the other people in the room and relax. I soon found some questions that I was more sure of but pushing the final accept button caused doubt in my mind in case the answer was wrong and that could be the one that could mean failure.

I must stop doubting myself and as the trainers were walking around they would say in a very quiet voice 'go with your gut feelings and trust your instincts do not keep doubting yourself'. Of course this was true and time was passing by, I had to make a decision and push accept and go for it. Everyone was starting to leave their computers and it seemed they had all finished but I wanted to use all the time to make sure I had not made any silly mistakes that would cost me the exam as some people had already done to their cost.

Finally, the time was up and I could do no more and the trainers were approaching to go into my computer to see whether I had failed or passed. I could hardly breathe, I felt so nervous waiting for those anxious seconds for the score to come up. I closed my eyes, I did not want to look, this was it. Congratulations you have scored 100% 'Well Done a really excellent exam result'. I could hardly believe my eyes but there was the result right in front of me and all that studying had been worth it. I would at last be getting my long awaited 'wings'.

Celebration was in order for most of us, some trainees had fallen by the wayside as if at any time you reached 5 points on your record for any failures or misdemeanors you would be asked to leave the course. These could be for not wearing the uniform correctly, failing any of the tests or generally feeling that cabin crew was not the job for them.

We were told that our 'wings' would be presented by the head of the Airline Company and we would then be told whether we would be flying out of Heathrow or Gatwick. In my heart, I so hoped it would be

Gatwick as it would make travelling so much easier but I was just so excited I could not wait to tell everyone that I was at long last Cabin Crew.

Another trip to Uniform Stores to be fitted for the remainder of the uniform required for cabin crew and then an appointment was made to visit the American Embassy to obtain a working and travel visa as this would be required for travelling in and out of American destinations. If anyone had any criminal convictions, the Americans would not grant the visa. It was such a shame but one of the trainees had been in trouble in his early youth and been put on probation which precluded him from obtaining a visa and therefore unable to operate longhaul flights. Unfortunately, after all the training he was unable to proceed any further. It just shows how a small misdemeanor in your younger years can affect you in later life.

Luckily I had not blotted my copy book along the way. I duly received my appointment along with all the others and once a CRB check was also applied for, we were on our way by coach to London. Whilst waiting outside the American Embassy in Grosvenor Square, we were surprised at how many recognisable people were in the queue and we could hear the dulcet tones of Betty Boothroyd, who was then Speaker of the House of Commons.

As I looked across the road I could see North Audley Street where I had worked as a temp when I first came to London at 17 and used to go to this very square to eat my lunch. I remembered being very scared as one day in 1968, the building where I worked along with all the other buildings in the area, including Selfridges and other big stores in Oxford Street, had to be boarded up as there was to be a huge Anti-Vietnam demonstration, which did in fact turn very violent. The noise was deafening and eventually, we were told to go home as it was all getting out of hand as 10,000 demonstrators were holding a rally in Trafalgar Square which was on my way to Charing Cross Station where I used to catch the train home.

Being young and having never seen anything like this before, the walk to the station was extremely scary. I decided that it did not matter how long it took but I would try and catch a bus, the few that were still able to run, as at least I would be with lots of other people all trying to get to the station.

It seemed such a long time ago as I recalled this episode in my mind and here I was some thirty years later standing outside the Embassy as soon to be cabin crew getting ready to fly to America on a regular basis. Such a lot had happened in my life since then, I could hardly believe that so many years had passed but I had finally achieved my early ambition and it just shows anything is possible, no matter how old you are. Now I was just waiting to be interviewed by the officials at the Embassy to enable my journey to begin.

After queuing for an hour it was my turn and if I ever felt guilty, it was now. As I was giving my answers, I felt I was being scrutinised and even though I was being completely truthful, I am sure I had guilt written all over my face. Eventually, I passed on all the questions I answered and went on to the next section to have my photos checked. What seemed to be an incredible length of time, the visas were granted and my passport was taken to have these attached, one step nearer.

I became more comfortable with this scrutiny as we would be going in and out of America and many other countries where, even though we are crew, we would still be the subject of border checks and have our baggage searched. Even on arrival back at home base, the Customs officers would sometimes be there to check all the crews baggage to make sure we were not bringing anything through illegally, such as drugs, or too many cigarettes and spirits above our legal allowance. They could even stop crew when we went to our cars in the airport car park on our way home therefore we were given very strict warnings on this front as the Airline would not back us if we broke these rules.

Likewise, if we were caught taking anything off the aircraft that did not belong to us, including any food that was due to be thrown away, duty free products or crew purchase (we would be able to buy miniaitures of alcohol at reduced rates from the bar) or if we were caught without a valid receipt, or taking more than our allowance, this would be a sackable offence.

It was really impressed upon us that the Airline Company would not stand by us but if caught in violation of Customs and Excise Rules, we were on our own and our employment would be terminated.

Certain positions on the aircraft would mean that the person would be in charge of one of the duty free trolleys that would go out during the flight. This responsibility would mean making sure it was opened correctly with all the relevant seals, the takings all accounted for and banked on return to base. Again failure to do this would result in being called upstairs to explain any shortfall.

A visit to Crawley to buy a navy hardshell large suitcases, together with an onboard wheelie bag which would hold everything required for the flight, was a light relief after all the information imparted about Duty Free security we had received during the last few days. We all went to the luggage shop and I soon realised that I would need a large suitcase for all the shopping I would be doing! This case together with the wheelie would have to be loaded and uploaded into my car, taken on the crew bus to crew report and checked-in where the large suitcase would go down to the aircraft. I knew a smaller suitcase would be more manageable and less strain on the arms. It is amazing, if packed correctly, how much a suitcase can house.

With the suitcases purchased, it was time to go for lunch and those of us that were left were now eagerly awaiting to find out which base we would all be allocated. Although we would seldom fly together, we had already exchanged mobile numbers so that we could keep in touch and let each other know how we were getting on. Claire and I were amazed at the camaraderie that existed between us, even though there was a large age difference, we had all spent the last six weeks together and despite some people falling by the wayside, most of us were pleased and relieved to have reached this point. Only the wings ceremony and base information was left.

Claire and I gave up our keys at the Hotel Reception desk and as we had been there so long we had become really friendly with the staff, although I have to say after six weeks in the same small room with all our cases and uniform, it would be really lovely to head home. Strange to think six weeks ago we arrived very daunted by what was ahead but we had hit all the challenges full on, although at times it would have been so easy to give up, and now we were leaving as cabin crew. I could hardly believe what I had been able to achieve with the swimming, the smoke-filled chamber and all the medical scenarios, I just hoped that I would not have to put some of these into practice.

I hardly slept that night and decided I might as well get up early as I would need to look immaculate, especially today, and leave plenty of time to get to Gatwick for the Wings Ceremony. I arrived at the Security Gate, which was the last time for a little while and suddenly it seemed everyone on the course was also parking their car. For the last time as a group, we started the day with a coffee in the canteen and then waited to be called upstairs, where we were aware that the Head of the Airline Company had arrived.

On reaching the Classroom, there was a 'whiteboard' that we knew would reveal the base we would be working from and in my heart, I hoped it would be Gatwick as the journey would be so much easier for me, less wear and tear on the car and much more familiar to me. We received praise from the trainers at this point and hoped that they had imparted as much information as was possible to start our flying career but the best way to learn was to put this all into practice by going on a flight.

The door opened and the 'big Boss' was welcomed in. I had, in fact, already met him when boarding an inaugural flight whilst I was on the ground so I recognised him straight away. He congratulated us on our success in passing, what after all, was a very tough training course and we now realised that it was not just a case of handing out 'chicken or beef', something that still follows me to this day when people find out that I was cabin crew.

The ground staff cloth wings had been removed and now in their place was a half silver wing, only the Captain and First Officers get the full pair of silver wings, but half would do me and it was more than I ever thought I would have. So after a few good wishes, it was back to the classroom where the whiteboard had the words uncovered and read "Longhaul Gatwick Fleet."

We could not believe our luck to have our wings and be based out of Gatwick. This was just the best result we could have all hoped for as this was everyone's first choice. It is strange how after all these years, now I am in my fifties, the new part of my life was just beginning and I could not wait to get on board to start putting all this training into practice.

I drove home in a daze of how I had actually reached this point having received my schedule for the month and my first trip would be to Cairo but this was leaving out of Heathrow. I was really excited but extremely anxious about how it would all work and whether I would remember everything.

I was at home now for a few days before I started flying. My parents could not believe I was going to do something so foolhardy at my age. I heard from Steve, one of the other trainees, and thankfully he too had been scheduled to go on this particular flight, so at least I would know someone on the crew.

CHAPTER 22

Cairo was only an overnight stop as it was only about 6 hours but deciding what to take and being able to manoeuvre a large suitcase together with my handbag and wheelie was going to take some practice. I must have packed and unpacked a hundred times, what to take, how hot would it be, what would be suitable clothing so as not to offend the locals and it seems I had a lot of clothing and shoes for a one night trip, so how was I going to manage on a 7 day trip?

Having sorted out the large suitcase with far too many clothes I was sure, I then had to work out what to put in the onboard wheelie. My gilet for actually carrying out the onboard meal service, a pair of flat sensible and very comfortable black court shoes to change into once the safety demonstration was about to commence, then my cardigan as we had been told it can become extremely cold at night onboard the aircraft. A tip from the trainers was a hot water bottle, which stayed in my wheelie bag for the whole of my flying career, it was like my trusted friend and later on my beloved sleeping bag, which I will tell you more about later on.

A separate wallet for the duty free monies, together with any documentation I might need to refer to, such as where I should be standing when the safety demonstration took place. If I put much more in my bags I knew I would never be able to lift them in and out of the car, so I decided just to take essentials and learn from other crew what was vital and what was not.

Steve seemed to be in the same turmoil, but being a guy he had decided to just take minimal warm weather clothes but he found out to his cost later on a jacket might have been more prudent.

We would both be picked up from Gatwick at the allotted time and driven to Heathrow where we would meet the remainder of the crew. We would not actually be working on the flight this would be like a 'supernumerary' flight where we would be extras and there to observe as it was our first time on board. Thank goodness for that as just the thought of going to Heathrow was extremely worrying.

As I lifted my suitcase and wheelie into the back of my car, I just knew I would need to be more minimalistic otherwise there would be no room for shopping. As I pulled both bags from the car to the crew bus, I knew I would need alot more practice at this. Over the years I did learn the art of pulling two bags, one of which would be extremely heavy, with some sort of elegance.

I met Steve on the crew bus and he looked just like I felt. We checked in at Gatwick and there waiting for us was a lovely black limousine to take us to Heathrow. The journey was a blur and I suddenly felt so nervous that I thought I might even be car sick. Steve, it seemed to be just as anxious as we drew up outside the crew report centre at Heathrow and we could see lots of other crew all reporting and knowing exactly what and where they were supposed to be going and doing.

We checked in and were told to report to a room allocated for the briefing where we would find the rest of our crew and the Senior who would give us all the information about the flight. I definitely needed to go to the toilet again although I had been umpteen times already, surely there was nothing left to come out! Supposing I could not answer the briefing questions and could not go on my first flight. Steve and I decided we would try and hopefully help each other, that is of course if either of us actually knew the answers.

We entered the room and at this point no one knew it was our first flight but this was all to change when the Cabin Manager introduced us and explained this was our first flight. Everyone looked kindly and sympathetically at us but I am sure they were thinking differently. Two members of the crew would 'buddy' us and generally show us the ropes which we were more than grateful for, perhaps they would answer the questions as well.

The Cabin Manager went around the room and it was then it all started to fall into place. The more senior you were, the choice of where you worked in the cabin was better. The lower down you were, the less choices you had and would be left with positions that no one wanted to work, which could be working in the Galley and supervising all the food or doing duty free that some crew hated. Whilst on other flights, everyone wanted to work down the back as they did not like working in the Club cabins and others loved working in the Galleys as they did not have so much contact with the passengers and loved food preparation.

My 'buddy' obviously knew where she wanted to be on the aircraft and was quite senior, so we would be working in Club World whilst Steve was working down the back to start with but we would change over during the flight so we both could get a taste of what the different positions involved.

Then came the dreaded questions, it was to be a scenario so the Cabin Manager would start "Suppose the aircraft was trundling down the runway when all of a sudden the aircraft came to a complete standstill," then each member of the crew would have to answer what happened next and go around the room with each stage. My mind was a complete blank and I was trying to work out when it reached my turn, what part of the story I would be at when the person next but one to me answered more and that meant my answer would be out of kilter.

Panic set in. The Cabin Manager must have seen how worried we were and he asked Steve and I a joint question which, luckily enough, we both remembered from our training.

Only medical questions to go now. 'What do we carry on board to help someone suffering from an asthma attack who does not have their medication, as they have packed it in their checked in suitcase, and then due to panic is unable to use our medication'. I remembered and could visualise the on board medical kit where the Ventolin Inhaler and the little spacer that we had to put together which incorporated the inhaler if the passenger had become too distressed, so I was able to answer my question. Steve got the question about the Epipen and how this should be applied and luckily he remembered how we had been told to administer the pen correctly otherwise the needle with the adrenaline might end up going into your own leg, which would cause your own leg to go numb and of course no use to the passenger. We had passed - this was to be one of many briefings during our flying career.

I never forgot how I felt at my first briefing and how daunting it all felt to come out of training and go on board for the first time. Over the years I suppose I took it for granted that I knew the different aircrafts inside and out, together with the different positions I liked to work and what the Company required of me.

The other crew were amazed at the size of our bags for just an overnight stay and when we saw how little they all took, we realised a scaling down would, in the future, be necessary as we looked as though we were going away for a month! I was glad to get rid of my huge suitcase, not only because of the weight but I am sure it caused great amusement to the other crew who were too nice to make further comment. Note to self - pack less.

Going on board the 777 seemed huge when all the seats were empty and I was so glad to follow my 'buddy' as she would show me where I could put my wheelie and hang up my clothes for the flight, ie gilet and onboard shoes. She would then show me where we would be sitting for the whole of the flight and how to carry out a full search and security check of that part of the aircraft before anything else was done.

During all this the Captain and the First Officer (only two of them required for a trip that was this short) arrived and introduced themselves to us. Again, I would learn throughout my flying career that at this point when the flight crew were undertaking security and routine checks on the aircraft, when to interrupt and when not to. More importantly, whether they required tea or coffee and in china or paper cups. Some Captains hated having paper cups and would only have china, whilst others preferred paper. As we had to make stipulated checks on the flight crew, it was very important that tea, coffee, snacks and meals were offered regularly.

95

Well, the Captain and First Officer seemed very nice and welcomed us and hoped we had a good first flight and perhaps Steve and I would like to go on the flight deck for take off and landing as the experience would be really worthwhile. Luckily I had remembered the code for going in and out of the flight deck and how it all worked so I would not disgrace myself with the flight crew once the door was closed for take-off.

Whilst the flight crew were getting prepared for the flight and doing their pre-flight checks, Claire explained that they would need their snacks, coffee or tea and newspapers to read during the flight and that if I worked in this part of the aircraft I would be responsible for looking after them for pre-take off and during the flight. Along with this, there were boarding drinks to pour ie. opening the champagne, orange juice and water and arranging the newspapers ready to give passengers in the Club cabin.

I soon realised just how busy this part of the flight was always going to be as passengers needed to be shown to their seats, jackets taken and hung up in the wardrobes and newspapers and drinks given to them all. Obviously, it was all agreed between the crew who was going to deal with all of the above as sometimes one side of the Club cabin would be busier than the other so it was a case of 'all hands to the pump'. There were also, as I remember from being at the boarding gate, many queries about seating and my previous job proved invaluable when sorting out seating discrepancies and problems.

Most passengers obviously want to be seated together but it seemed on certain flights everyone wanted the window and others the aisle and there seemed to be no pattern to it at all, except that it was the leg room that was the most important factor. Although business people who wanted to work did not want to have to sit anywhere near families and therefore the boarding process could be quite fraught, discretion was a huge part of this procedure as I did not fancy having to tell an already exasperated mother that her children were making too much noise, especially if the child just happened to be a tiny baby. After all the families had paid just as much for their Club seats.

No wonder the whole process took over an hour to complete as I looked on in amazement, between serving passengers and making sure the flight crew were okay, I felt I was running around like a headless chicken. Suddenly the doors were closed, we were almost ready to push back and Claire explained this would be a good time to change my shoes and hang up my jacket as the Safety demonstration was about to take place. I had never done this in front of passengers, only my colleagues, and Claire kindly said she would do it this time and I could watch so I was more prepared for carrying this out on the way home, for which I was so grateful as on the journey home it would be dark and perhaps no-one would notice my mistakes!

The time had gone by so quickly that I was in a complete daze trying to take it all in. I could feel the aircraft lurch as it moved away from the jetty under its own steam now - the flight deck door was about to be shut 'Had I cleared the flight deck and collected in all the china as this was extremely important before take off as it would not be a good idea to have this flying around' said Claire. I must remember to do this and then suddenly the call was made by the Cabin Manager 'Doors to Automatic and Cross Check' and I knew the aircraft slides were in position and we were almost ready to depart and Claire impressed upon me that this procedure was vital as failure to do this could result in a serious accident and disciplinary action.

I watched as Claire placed the huge doors into Automatic and then crossed over to the other side of the aircraft and made sure her opposite crew member had done the same, then waited for the call to come from the Cabin Manager to check from all the left-hand crew had done the same. When the 'bing bong' and the pink light illuminated, Claire imparted this information and likewise the other left-hand crew, something I was going to have to get used to doing, then it was into position to carry out the 'demo'.

Claire showed me where I would find the 'demo' equipment and she explained it would be a good idea to get everything out of the pouch to make sure it was all there. She explained there was nothing worse than hearing the voice on the tape asking you to look at the safety card or to pull the lifejacket over your head and finding one of these items was missing. I had made so many 'Note to Self' I could fill two notebooks but it was vital to have these tips.

With the safety demo over it was time to check that all the passengers were safe and secure in their seats, making sure the galley was clear so that nothing could come crashing out, including securing the trolleys otherwise the next thing you know a trolley would be rolling past you and building up speed through the cabin, much to passengers horror.

The call was then made for 'Cabin Crew to take their seats for take off' and as I secured my seatbelt I heaved a sigh of relief that boarding was over and we were finally on our way. My First trip as Cabin Crew was about to commence.

CHAPTER 23

There I was, at long last, strapped into my seat and taxiing down the runway about to take off to Cairo. I felt so exhilarated as I could see we were at the end of the runway with other aircrafts in front of us as we lined up to take our turn. We slowly moved forward until the aircraft turned to take its position as obviously we were next in the queue. With a huge surge of power, the 777 engines roared with force as we raced down the runway building up speed until suddenly she just lifted off the ground majestically and started the climb into the sky.

It had always been a wonder to me how such a huge lump of metal, carrying all the passengers and tons of luggage and cargo, can actually lift so elegantly into the sky climbing and leaving the airport and car parks below until the clouds took the aircraft out of sight. I looked out of the window until it was only possible to see the land below through the thickening clouds and I could just make out the Houses of Parliament and the Thames, which looked so completely different from the air as it wound its way under the many bridges and out of sight.

The Cabin Manager welcomed the passengers on board, via the intercom system, giving them details of the service in the different cabins and that when the seatbelt signs came on they must return to their seats and strap in for safety reasons. By this time the aircraft had levelled out and we were told that it was safe for us to get out of our seats, which seemed all too soon to me as I was quite happy just sitting there taking it all in, we were able to start moving around.

On-board gilets were then put on for the service which would commence with the drinks trolley being set up and going out so that passengers could have their long awaited 'first' drink. Although I suspected that most passengers had already had their first drink or two in the Club Lounge but the drinks trolley was always eagerly awaited after takeoff it appeared.

I soon learned from Claire how the trolley was set up, along with the passenger list so that we could use passengers names on the rows that I would be serving. Usually one on each end of the trolley and the passengers facing you would be the ones you would serve, although in my case Claire seemed to do an awful lot more as I was obviously not quite up to speed.

My passengers were all so lovely and wanted to chat, especially when they knew it was my first flight. Then there was the decision over what to drink, tasting of the different wines, whilst Claire's passengers knew what they wanted to drink and so she was able to move much faster than me. I seemed to have the passengers who having seen me mix my first 'Bloody Mary', decided that looked so good they would also have one, which obviously took longer than just pouring a glass of wine.

During the two drinks rounds, the meal orders were being taken and hearing how passengers were complaining that they had not been able to have their first choice of meal, I knew this part of the service could be tricky as the aircraft was only catered with so many meals. Sometimes everyone wanted the fish, then next flight everyone wanted the steak or pasta, so this part of the service was obviously going to be challenging and I realised why the crew did not particularly like this as it could be very confrontational.

I found whilst handing out meals and pouring the wine was easy on the ground during training, it was alot more difficult with the aircraft movement, especially if there was any turbulence. If the seatbelt signs were put on by the Captain then everyone was required to return to their seats and no hot drinks would be served for safety reasons so as not to scold anyone, crew or passengers. Having returned to their seats we had to stop what we were doing immediately and check all the passengers to make sure they had their seatbelts on and then confirm this to the Senior, who in turn would relay this to the flight crew.

Turbulence caused great anxiety for many of the passengers, they immediately thought that the aircraft was going to crash and so I could see why we had been taught to stay calm and smile. By looking unconcerned, the passengers would know from our faces that there was nothing to worry about and I could now see how reassuring this would prove to be. The worse part from the crews point of view is all the complaints about when the seatbelt sign was going off as they suddenly desperately needed the toilet, or that the tea and coffee part of the service had been temporarily suspended and when would it be resumed.

Wth the service over and before passengers settle down for their afternoon siesta, it was time to go out on the Duty Free trolley with Claire. This was the first time, since we had come on board, that I had actually seen Steve as he came with his 'buddy' to open the Duty Free trolleys.

"How was it going," I asked him. He, like me, found there was so much to think about and put into practise. I suddenly realised that during the whole service, I had been concentrating so much I had completely forgotten to check on the flight crew. They could have collapsed from lack of drink and food, although I think there might have been some signs from the aircraft that all was not well, but still, I realised I had relied on Claire carrying out the checks, which was something I must get to grips with. Although we were only supposed to be observing on this flight, the crew were happy for us to assist if we felt able, as hands on was the best way to learn.

The Duty Free service was really busy with people taking advantage of the cheap cigarettes, drink and cosmetics and there were four operators who were responsible for two bars each. This was the first time I had seen the machines in action, making sure the goods and money were correct was important as discrepancies had to be accounted for before the duty free bars were closed at the end of each flight. Anyone paying in foreign currency would receive the change in our own British currency and Claire explained that sometimes this was where mistakes could be found. I was quite happy to find the different items in the catalogue whilst she dealt with the money side but as the other three operators would also need me to find items only stocked in the Club two bars, which meant we were pretty busy.

Luckily before crew were allowed to sit down to have something to eat, all the duty free had to be completed so Claire explained most flights everyone would help. In the early days the bar operators and the Senior on the flight received two shares and the remaining crew one share of the total monies taken. (Sadly this altered as time went on and everyone only received one share towards the end, making the position of duty free less attractive). At the end of each flight all the crew were given a receipt with how much we would receive in our pay, which on some flights could be very lucrative, as many items in the catalogue, especially in Club, could cost £200 or £300 an item. This would help with the fuel for my car.

I had forgotten all about food but I was actually feeling hungry now and ready to sit down. One thing I learned very quickly, the reason for the comfy onboard shoes was because of the time we were on our feet. M & S always came to the rescue as I always bought the same 'footglove' padded leather shoes, as at the end of each flight my feet would swell up and stretch the shoes. They were like boats when my feet were cooler and although most of the crew kept their shoes in a shoebag and despite plenty of different sprays, going into the wardrobe was seldom a pleasant experience! Apparently these shoes and certain other personal items were very saleable on ebay, mine were only fit for the bin.

As this was a short trip, the rest break would only be short and was taken in the crew seats by the doors. I now realised why sleeping bags and hot water bottles were going to be a godsend, especially during the night as it was extremely cold and draughty sleeping behind the curtain at the doorway.

The crew at the back slept in the last rows of the aircraft which was also far from comfortable but it is something we all got used to doing as we were glad to get off our feet and rest. Rest was taken in two halves, as half the crew would have to be on duty whilst the others went to rest as some passengers remained awake and juice rounds had to be undertaken at least every hour to make sure passengers were kept hydrated. Toilets had to be checked and of course, it was a matter of safety that crew were vigilant, even more so at night in many ways as that was often the time when passengers who had been on holiday became unwell for instance.

I finally checked in with the flight crew and they asked if I would like to come onto the flight deck for landing in Cairo, which I jumped at the chance of doing. Then it was time to sit and read my notes for half an hour on my rest break, although it was not long until we were ready for landing. There were still all the bars that had to be counted and the paperwork prepared ready for customs and restocked for the way home flight.

Afternoon tea seemed to be alot easier than the main lunch service as it was just sandwiches and scones with tea, plus champagne if required. However, we would soon be getting the 40 minutes to landing call from the flight crew so it would not be long before we would be getting the cabins prepared for landing. So I was asked to go and assist down the back with clearing in the tea and getting the cabin secure.

When I walked through the cabin to the back it was just a sea of faces and I could not believe how messy it was. You could hardly see the floor in places and I often wondered if passengers treated their own homes in this way by just discarding all their rubbish on the floor. At night it was so easy to be walking through the cabin doing our checks only to slip on a glossy magazine someone had left on the floor.

40 minutes did not seem nearly enough to prepare for landing as passengers always seemed to need the toilet at the last minute but somehow with all the crew pulling together when the 20 minute call came, everyone was secured in their seats, the floor cleared and tidy, bassinets and chairs for babies all folded down and safely stowed.

When I returned to the front of the aircraft, the Club passengers were safely secured with their seatbelts on and it just remained for the wine and champagne that had been opened to be poured down the toilets, yes all those expensive wines and champagne down the pan!! We were not allowed to land with any of the bottles opened, not only for the mess it would make if it spilt on landing but for customs regulations. It really went 'against the grain' to see all that wine going to waste and I did not even drink!

As time went by, however, to save costs and waste, the wines were recorked and the white wine placed in the chiller and the red wine placed in a container, to be used on the flight home. This procedure was not allowed when landing into the UK for customs reasons.

The Captain then asked the Cabin Manager if the aircraft was ready, whether I would like to go on the flight deck to see the aircraft land into Cairo as darkness was beginning to fall and the lights and sunset would make this worth seeing. I might not get another chance to do this as when I was a fully working member of the crew with door responsibilities and it was always very busy at this point securing the aircraft for landing. I was more than happy to take up this opportunity.

Arriving on the flight deck was very daunting as at this point there was a lot of work going on between the Captain, First Officer and the Tower in respect of our landing. I was told to strap myself into the extra seat securely as obviously they did not want me falling out of my seat across the controls. This might seem a very simple process but the strap that went between my legs was not very elegant with a pencil straight skirt on but I somehow managed. Then I was told by the Captain to put on the headset so I could hear what was being said by the 'Tower'.

There was so much going on it was difficult to take it all in. I was trying to listen to the instructions given by the Tower, then look at the amazing sunset and then we were given final instructions on our approach and it was decided that the First Officer would be landing the aircraft on this occasion. We descended to make our final approach, the views of the pyramids was absolutely breathtaking, I was not sure what to look at first. Suddenly there in front of me were the lights of the landing strip, which were stretched out in front of us lighting the way like sparkling jewels, for what seemed like miles enabling this huge aircraft to land.

The droning voice of the woman on the computer was now giving the countdown and the First Officer, who had been handed over the controls, was ready in the correct position for a smooth landing. As the aircraft slowly dropped lower and lower, I felt like I was in a car but on the side with no controls and even though my feet were pushing to the floor, nothing was happening. The ground and the edge of the lights suddenly appeared very near as the aircraft made that last little drop and there in front of me loomed the ground which felt we were going to crash into as the aircraft lowered itself onto the tarmac with such precision and then with quite a force the wheels touched the ground, which I must say even though it was a smooth landing, was quite a force - I was so glad I was securely belted in! The aircraft continued along the tarmac at great speed and I was aware of the First Officer pulling back on the brakes and the roar of the engines suddenly became very loud, then gradually died away as the aircraft started to slow down.

I remembered thinking just how long was this landing strip and whether we would ever stop, but the aircraft finally slowed down and we were told to turn off and taxi to our stand. The final preparations for attaching the aircraft to the jetty were given and as we made our way I could hear one of the crew making an announcement advising passengers that we had landed in Cairo and that she hoped they would have an enjoyable holiday or if they were arriving home, a safe onward journey. I would one day be in the crew position that would be making this call and it had to be done at the correct time so that the Captain could also address the passengers and hope they had enjoyed their flight and look forward to welcoming them on board again in the near future.

I suddenly realised I was still strapped in my seat and sitting there slightly shell-shocked as the Captain asked 'If I had enjoyed the landing as this was one of the more impressive destinations for scenery'. I felt like I was a school child being asked questions after a school outing, it was just the most amazing experience I had ever had and I was lost for words, which is a first for me!

Doors to Manual and Cross Check we had arrived in Cairo and I had survived my first flight as Cabin Crew. How lucky was I as this was now my new job, it was not going to be easy but having waited this long I felt I could meet the challenge.

I finally managed to winch myself out of the seat, the lapstrap was definitely challenging and I did not want to give the Captain and First Officer an eyeful of my underwear, thank goodness I decided against wearing stockings and suspenders! I made my escape thanking them profusely and realised how excited children would feel, back in those days, to be invited onto the flight deck by the Captain and look on in amazement at all the controls on the panel in front of them. For security reasons this seldom happens these days.

By this time the passengers were beginning to collect their bags and leave the aircraft, Club always left first, then World Traveller Plus then the remainder of the passengers who were alot more and had further to come. I loved being at the door saying 'Goodbye' to them and hoping they had an enjoyable trip as it was only on boarding and leaving the aircraft were we able to see all the passengers.

Most passengers at this point were delighted to be leaving the aircraft and were full of anticipation about their holiday, or just relieved to be home if they actually lived at the destination. Once all the passengers were off, it was then up to the crew to check the whole aircraft to make sure that nothing had been left and make sure all the overhead lockers were clear to make life easier for the cleaners, as it was always a mammoth task to clean and turn the aircraft around.

Having thanked Claire and the rest of the crew, it was then time to pack our onboard wheelies and with jackets on, with the Captain and First Officer at the helm we would all leave the aircraft together and walk through the airport to Passport Control and Baggage Reclaim. Most Passport Controls had a special lane for the crew so that we could get through more quickly, collect our luggage and get to the hotel transport. It was then that I managed to catch up with Steve and exchange details of how we felt our first flight went and to collect our huge luggage from the baggage reclaim belt and head towards the waiting hotel bus bay.

The hotel bus was always looked for eagerly as by this time crew had usually been on their feet for some considerable time and it was lovely to get to the Hotel Reception, check-in and get our room keys.

Steve and I decided on the bus that we would get to our rooms and have an early night, although it was already quite late, then start off first thing in the morning. We were due to fly out again later the following evening so we would not have long to explore this beautiful and interesting place. The First Officer, Glen, overheard our conversation and asked if we would mind if he tagged along with us as this was his first trip to Cairo. So we agreed we would meet for breakfast in the hotel at 7 am and arrange with the hotel for a car to pick us up and take us to the places of interest.

CHAPTER 24

Arrival at the hotel was breathtaking, it was an absolutely stunning hotel and we could not believe we were actually going to stay in such a wonderful place. Just the entrance hall was beautiful and once we had checked in we all went our separate ways to our allocated rooms. When I opened the door I could not believe how sumptuous it was, the fabrics, the decor and the bed looked very inviting and I knew if I was to just lay down for a few minutes I would soon be asleep, which would be fatal. So I decided to hang up my uniform and head for the shower but before I could do this, the phone rang and it was Steve. He also could not believe how lovely this hotel was and could not wait to sink into the huge double queen bed.

I decided from now on I would always firstly turn the security lock and put the bolt across on my door and just make a note of the emergency exits from my room in the event of a fire as we had been told to do whilst in training. A shower was next and then, having set the alarm for tomorrow morning, make a cup of tea (I always took my travel kettle, teabags and cup on any trip I was going on). I did this throughout my whole flying career, it was like a comfort blanket.

Before I retired to sleep I always ironed my white shirt ready for the trip home, just in case the iron was not working, or something came off the iron and dirtied by a beautiful white shirt. Nothing worse than getting the 'wake up' call an hour before pick up only to find the iron was not working - panic - as hotels did not always react too quickly to having to produce an iron at speed. Even though I always ironed and packed my shirts very carefully, I always needed to iron them to make sure they were in pristine condition.

I also learned from other crew that some of the cabin crew Mums used to take all their family ironing away with them in their suitcases, and on a night stop but mostly longer trips, enabled them to do a weeks ironing. They would then return home with all the ironing for the week done in their downtime so they could spend more time with their children on their days off. I hate ironing but never ever quite got into this practice as ironing on a trip was just as bad as doing it at home!

During my flying career, I found that crew were, if nothing, very resourceful with their down route time especially if they had visited the places on many occasions and did not want to spend their allowances for the trip. They took food to prepare in their rooms, although in most locations, apart from America, the hotel breakfast was included or we received an allowance. However most credit cards were fairly well used, so to save money, crew would take pot noodles etc. On one trip

I remembered baked beans going into a kettle to heat them up, not a pretty sight.

Sleep came very easily, even though it was a strange place, I was so tired and was awoken by the sound of my ever faithful alarm clock, which again would be going everywhere with me as I did not want to oversleep, or miss the pick up call.

I soon realised from the heat that was coming through the window that I would not be needing half the clothes I had packed, in fact, I would not be needing three-quarters of the items I had packed, a smaller bag for ease of packing and lifting was needed. Although I have to admit the destinations where shopping was involved, I would definitely need a big bag.

We had been told by the trainers to make sure we always wore suitable clothing for the destination as we had to be respectful of different cultures in respect of not revealing too much flesh, which would have been difficult for me as I did not like revealing too much flesh at home, especially the tops of my arms, so no fear there! I decided on knee length shorts, a tee shirt and a cardigan which I could tie around my waist which I could use as a cover up from my extensive packed wardrobe, and a small backpack as I knew we would have to be careful with our money.

Suitably dressed, I hoped, I rang Steve to see if he was ready and we agreed to meet in the restaurant for breakfast in 5 minutes. I was so glad he was on this trip as he was a big, burly guy and I felt more comfortable going out in this very busy area with him, together with Glen, and I could sandwich myself between them. All joking aside this was going to be very appropriate once outside.

Steve and Glen arrived at the same time as myself and we waited to be seated on the crew tables in this magnificent restaurant. Some of the other crew were there and wondered where we were off to so early. They had done this trip so many times and they would just be having a day around the pool in the sun instead.

After breakfast, we were advised by reception that our car (I loosely use this terminology) was waiting. It originally must have been a very nice car but was covered in dents and looked as though it had been in a banger race. As soon as we set off we realised why. The driving in Cairo is extremely bad, there are so many cars and they drive so fast and extremely close to pedestrians. I sat in the back between Steve and Glen and the driver asked if one of them would like to sit in the front, both declined his offer.

As we sped along the dusty roads woe betide anyone who stepped foot on the road as the cars went so quickly and close to them, I was surprised more people had not lost their lives. It seemed the cars weaved in and out and drive so close to one another, hence the dents in the cars, I will not be so quick to criticise the driving on the M25 in the future. I was so pleased to be anchored between the guys.

First stop was a guided tour around the museum where we were to see the famous Tutankhamun exhibition and of course the Mask. As we stood outside waiting for our guide, I could hardly believe my luck that my first trip would bring me to see one of my favourite parts of history enabling me to tick one item off my bucket list, and I was actually at work!!

The guide approached and luckily spoke relatively good English so the tour was just amazing. I could have spent hours in there, the dark areas where the original Mummies are stored and then to come face to face literally with the Tutankhamun mask is breathtaking. In fact, I got so close I managed to bang my face on the glass, much to the amusement of the security guards and the boys. There is something so compelling about the face and eyes on the mask, I could only marvel, as I did throughout the day at how clever they were in those days, how did that have such knowledge?

With the Museum over, our next destination was the market, which was very interesting but the begging of the children was heartbreaking and our children thankfully have no idea of how lucky they are. When you give to one child, hundreds of others seem to turn up and surround you. We decided that we should probably move on as time was going so quickly and there was so much to see.

We got back in the car and drove way out into the desert where our next stop was a ride on a camel, something I was not quite sure about but at least I had worn the correct clothes. It was extremely dusty and unfortunately, this started off Steve's asthma and despite his inhaler, it was proving too much for him and I did not want to have to call on my medical training this early. So the next best thing was a ride on a cart pulled by a donkey, which I have to say was only slightly better, as every time the driver hit the donkey with his whip, clouds of dust hit the air and started Steve off again. Luckily the donkey did not hang around and I could see the pyramids in the distance so we did not have far to go, thank goodness.

As we drew closer to the pyramids you can only look on in wonderment at just how clever the Egyptians were. How on earth were they able to build such magnificent structures that have managed to stand the test of time and I could not wait to explore them. Once the cart stopped, we jumped off and were confronted by huge numbers of men, women and children begging and it was extremely hard not to want to give them all some money but I knew once you give to one more would replace them.

By this time Steve had just about regained regular breathing but I could tell the dust was getting to him so it was good that the next part of our trip was to go down into the pyramids. Once again good use of my clothing as my skorts (shorts covered by a skirt, big in America) would mean I would not be bearing my underwear to Glen as the steps down were extremely steep and the head height meant we were virtually bent in two. Definitely not a good look as Steve went in front in case I should lose my footing, whilst Glen brought up the rear, literally, as my behind would be virtually in his face much to his amusement.

We seemed to be going down for a very long time and it was lucky that the lights guided the pathway and I had at least worn sensible shoes as flip flops would have made this impossible. When we finally reached the bottom, the inside of the pyramid was truly amazing, how on earth did they have the strength and 'know how' to create these wonderful structures. Everything about this truly wonderful place with its history was endless and I only wished we had more time to explore.

We then had to make the climb back up to the surface which in many ways was much tougher on the legs, but it was certainly very good exercise. Having reached the surface the extreme heat burned into our skin, as it was lovely to be inside the pyramid where it was cooler and less dusty. The guys had been laughing at me all day about the fact I had my cardigan with me but I was to have the last laugh. Our driver was back with us and we would be going on a sightseeing trip around the city, the boys wanted to go to the local Macdonalds to see how it differs from ours at home so this meant going right into the city.

On our way, I saw many people walking by the side of the road almost jumping for their lives and one woman decided to step off the pavement and I swear we missed her by inches. I therefore decided that I rarely eat MacDonalds, only with my children when I am at home, so I resisted the urge to go with the guys and I also thought I would not want to disgrace myself as I had already felt a bit queasy. I definitely would not want to see a cheeseburger or 'Bigmac' at close quarters in the back of the car. The guys nearly found this to their cost as we continued our trip over the very rough terrain!!

As darkness fell, the last part of our trip was to watch the Son et Lumiere show which was a sound and light show entertainment at Giza. With the darkness came the extreme drop in temperature and I was so glad to have bought my cardigan. Steve and Glen still only had their teeshirts on and as we sat down I noticed I was in the middle and they were huddled up to me as I was nice and warm - who had the last laugh now!!

I cannot do justice to this really spectacular pyrotechnic show which would light up the pyramids and sphinx whilst a dramatised narration of the history boomed out, in a slightly spooky voice. This was not to be missed, despite the cold, so I would always advise warmer clothes for this event.

We had very little time left until we would have to report for our return trip so sadly we had to return to our hotel, where the remainder of the crew were virtually still sitting in the same seats by the pool. They could not believe how long we had been out and how filthy we looked but it was so worth it as we had had a wonderful day and I hoped to bring JP with me next time so he could experience these wonderful sites.

The call for 'pick up' was always made by reception, one hour before our transport arrived, wherever we were staying and always in the time of the country. I had decided I would always keep my watch at the time it was in the UK, which helped when I made contact with home, which I always did, just to make sure all was well. This was something I did throughout my flying career just in case there was some crisis at home that required me to return home sooner, although I knew JP would deal with minor problems.

Luckily the flight home was only just under 5 hours so all I needed to do was stand in the shower and wash all the dirt and sand off. As I had already ironed and pressed my uniform, I just had to throw a few items in my suitcase, do my make-up and hair and I was ready to go. The crew would all meet downstairs in the hotel foyer and the bus would then drive us back to the airport to fly home. The time had gone so quickly and I realised how tired I now was, no wonder crew used to go and have a rest before flying home but there was so much to see that I did not want to miss anything by sleeping. I probably would not be saying this in the early hours of the morning.

CHAPTER 25

It was a strange feeling boarding passengers late at night, they were tired and just wanted to eat and get some sleep which really applied to most return flights, passengers liked to have as much sleep as possible as it made the return journey quicker. However, alot of passengers did not sleep but just watched films.

It was my turn to go down the back of the aircraft and Steve to go up the front. It was so completely different, there was certainly not the pressure on boarding as it was mainly always making sure someone was at the doors in case the aircraft had to be evacuated and dealing with the passengers to make sure they were in their correct seats and the ever increasing problems of hand luggage. Some passengers would bring hand baggage the same size as their checked in luggage and as it was so heavy I used to wonder just what was in the bags, they weighed a ton! We were told not to lift passengers bags as constantly doing this could result in back injuries.

I helped in World Traveller Plus with the pouring of their drinks and newspapers but apart from lots of seating queries, it was all pretty quiet. Whilst at the front, I could see Steve was really busy. Boarding complete, doors all armed, now came the safety demonstration that I was dreading. At least it was night time and hopefully passengers would be too tired to take much notice.

Shoes changed, demo equipment out and checked, it was all there luckily and it was a good tip from Claire. I was now standing in the correct position for my very first live demo. First the card, yes that was fine, until I turned it around to do the pointing out only to find it was upside down! Exit doors and oxygen masks were all fine, then came the dreaded bright yellow lifejacket. There was nowhere to hide, I could hear the voice saying 'pass it over your head' which was easier said than done with my hair piled up and having to remain immaculate, 'pass the tapes around your waist and tie them securely in a double bow at the side'. Whilst I was doing the double bow, this gave me a quick chance to catch up, much to the amusement of the passengers in the front row who unfortunately were not at all sleepy and watching intently.

The voice then moved on to 'there is a tube here for further inflation of the life jacket and a light and whistle for attracting attention, pull the red toggle as shown which will inflate the life jacket but do not pull this until you are outside the aircraft' which I had certainly done as everyone seemed to be watching me quite intently. Luckily, to secure the passengers, the crew always kept on the lifejacket which I was pleased about as I could go to the back galley and rearrange my hair. I explained to some of the amused passengers that this was my first trip and I had never done this in front of a live audience, it was like being on stage and doing a quick change. I would go to the galley and come out looking immaculate, maybe, time allowing, and they were all so lovely and said 'it had made their flight'. Not quite sure what that meant but at least we were all laughing.

I often thought back to this first flight as over the years I had carried out so many safety demos that I had lost count and unbelievably after a few goes it is really easy. I had not realised that this procedure changed if the system went down and the automatic demonstration turned into the crew member, at a certain position on the aircraft, having to read it. This crew member would not only be responsible for all the intercom boarding announcements, ie. Welcome on board, 40 minute and 20 minute calls, but also the landing call. Landing calls could be tricky if you were not prepared as, like all the calls, they had to be read from specific instructions laid down in the Announcement booklet given by the Company and not deviated from, as some crew liked to add their own little variation! It was important to make this particular call when the aircraft had landed and turned off the main runway and was heading towards the arrival gate. Failure to make this call at the right time would result in the captain being unable to make his farewell announcement to the passengers. Announcing the correct times at the landing destination was also important. Another 'note to self' to get this sorted before reading.

The service down the back was very different and I soon realised that once this started how very different it was from the front, obviously there were so many more people to deal with, firstly with drinks and then with the meal service. The trolleys when loaded were extremely heavy so one person on each end helped. It put a new slant on 'chicken or beef' having to pull the trays out carefully and it seemed no-one wanted the chicken and everyone wanted beef or pasta and as we reached the middle where all the four trolleys would meet, there would be no choice, which I could see was going to be a problem. Especially with vegetarian passengers who had not ordered a special meal.

This was the first insight I had into the problems experienced throughout the aircraft with the amount of food taken on board. Whatever the caterers loaded, it would be impossible to cater for everyone's needs, as it depends on the day and quite obviously passengers get so annoyed when they feel they have paid all this money and do not get their first choice of a meal. The aircraft is limited to the amount of food that can be loaded and once airborne there is no way of sending out for more supplies, unlike a restaurant.

Trying to explain the above was sometimes an uphill struggle as we cannot produce more food out of thin air. Despite how much passengers shouted at us, and believe me did they shout, all we were able to do was write an onboard form requesting more beef or more chicken next time!

Once the meal service and duty free had been completed, it was time for us to have our dinner as most of the passengers were bedding down for the night. We were then able to sit down for a break which was shared out amongst the crew but on a short flight like this, it would not be long. Once the lights went down on the aircraft and the paperwork for the bars were completed, it did not seem very long before the breakfast service was being carried out and we were preparing to land.

It was just lovely being in my crew seat again, as tiredness was beginning to creep in and seeing the landing lights as dawn was just beginning to break as we came into land, I realised my first flight was over and we were home. With the passengers disembarked it just remained to thank all the crew for their help, passing through passport control and collecting our luggage and hoping we were not stopped by customs as this would delay our journey home.

Glen, our First Officer, said his goodbyes and we said we would exchange photos of our wonderful trip. By this time we were absolutely shattered and just pleased to see the Captain and First Officer's car arrive, together with the car to take Steve and I back to Gatwick. Almost immediately Steve and I fell asleep in the back of the car and were glad that the traffic was bad as it would give us more time to sleep before we had to drive our own cars back home. It seemed like I had only just closed my eyes when the driver was telling us we were back at base and Steve and I decided we needed to check our rosters for the month and go and have a coffee before getting the crew bus back to our cars.

Coffee became priority and we sat in the coffee shop like two zombies, would we ever get used to being awake all night, and this had only been a short trip. I had already decided at this early stage that I really much preferred working up the front and Steve said he was happier down the back as it was not so exacting. Not at this stage would we have much choice as we would, for the foreseeable future, be at the bottom of the crew list. All we could think about now was getting to our cars and staying awake enough to get home safely.

When we reached our cars, having said our goodbyes and agreeing to exchange photos, Steve and I agreed that it had been a wonderful first trip, as this time yesterday we were in Cairo at the Museum and now we were back in England and on our way home.

In all my years of flying, I never flew with Steve again, although we did keep in contact.

It was true what the trainers had told us that staying awake all night, even with crew rest, would take six months for the body to adjust. So driving the one and a half hours home would always be quite difficult as tiredness suddenly comes across you like a veil and I found many ways of keeping my eyes open, as I knew if I closed them for just a few seconds it would be enough to either cause an accident or leave the road. Therefore falling asleep at the wheel was not an option, so it was strong coffee on landing, singing along with the window wound down (heaven knows what people thought as they passed by, especially unsuspecting pedestrians) but as needs must.

During my flying career, I only closed my eyes whilst driving on two occasions. One was just for a second as I was in the last 10 minutes of my journey, which was always the worse time as my concentration was not good as I knew home was in sight, but as I hit the curb, my goodness the adrenalin kicked in and it gave me such a jolt that I soon woke up. It is surprising how far you travel off course in that short space of time.

The other incident was when I stopped at the roadworks, about 20 minutes from home. They were three way and it seemed to be red forever. I was suddenly awoken to the sound of someone hooting and I realised, in the lovely sunshine, I had fallen asleep at the lights and there was no one in front of me!

I therefore decided for safety reasons, I would make a regular 'pitstop' at Waitrose on my way home where I would pick up bread and milk, which I knew they would be short of at home, whilst I could have my halfway free coffee which would keep me going. I was well known at this venue as obviously everyone recognised the uniform and the usual question would always be 'where have you just flown in from' or even worse 'where are you just flying off to'. This could have been taken in one of two ways, as having not slept, make-up and hair not at its best, how could people have thought I was just going to work? Maybe they were just being polite.

Turning into the driveway was always absolute bliss and I was home safely, it is true when they say there is no place like home. Everyone was out, so my little ritual was to take my bags inside, put the kettle on and then make my way upstairs taking my uniform off as I went. Uniform hung up, dirty washing loaded in the washing machine, a cup of tea poured and then to stand under the shower for at least 10 minutes to get rid of the smell of the aircraft.

If it was before 9 am, I would make myself some porridge and then go to sleep for a couple of hours. If it was later then I would try and stay up and go to bed by 9 or 10 o'clock at the latest, but I have to say by 6 pm I was usually hanging if I had had no sleep and been awake the previous night. It would take at least two nights to get back into a proper sleep pattern for me then it was back on duty again, as in the early days we had three days off between flights.

CHAPTER 26

Of course, flying away does not make the problems that have arisen and were there before I went off, go away. Unfortunately, they are still there waiting for me to try and get my head around. I just hoped my roster would mean that I would be earning good money as I certainly needed it to support the debts that I still had and to keep a roof over our heads, although my girls had moved into flats but I still had my son living at home as he was at college.

When I checked my roster I saw that I had a Houston trip for four days, a back to back Barbados/Bermuda which was a seven day trip and a three day Dallas.

Houston was one of my favourites, although it was a long flight of 10 to 11 hours & especially in the Winter, we received extra money because of this. Then the back to back would mean three days in Barbados and then bringing the flight home. A night stop in a hotel near Gatwick airport would mean I would sleep for a few hours then go shopping in Crawley.

The next morning, the transport would arrive to take us back to finish the trip, which in my case was a three days in Bermuda, again lucky for me as it was really good money. As well as receiving a flat wage, all the destinations were paid as flight pay and were added to my wages, obviously the longer trips paid more together with the seven or eight day back to backs which were shared out amongst the crew so that everyone got their fair share of profitable destinations.

Everyone had their favourite trips and I loved the American trips, especially for the shopping. The red and white plastic 'Target' bags were very much a part of crews luggage, together with Bath and Body Works bags. Crew were a wonderful advertisement for both stores, along with many other outlets and we were very lucky that most of the hotels, where the crew stayed, ran a shuttle bus to the shops for us.

I still found the crew briefings quite daunting as I was so afraid that I would not be able to answer the questions when it came to my turn. It would be dreadful to fail and not be able to go on the flight. I found some Cabin Managers made the briefings easier to put crew at their ease and as the months went by I got to know more of them as we would go out when we were down route either shopping or having breakfast. Very often some of us would get together in the evenings, so gradually I was getting to know how easy a trip would be as their name would appear on our rosters.

I could not believe that my first six months probation had passed by so quickly and I had my first appraisal whereby I had been monitored on each flight and then my Manager would tell me whether I had done well enough to be taken on permanently. I had actually forgotten this part so when I was asked to have a meeting with my Manager, it suddenly dawned on me that I might soon be looking for another job. However, all seemed to have gone down well, especially in regards to my interaction with the passengers, which to me was the part I loved the most.

I was to be made permanent - what a relief!

Even being made permanent, this was still dependent on keeping up with the year recurrent SEP training and this year it was decided that we should have extra training which would include terriorist training.

I was not sure what form this would take but it was to prepare us for what to look for in a passenger, anyone acting suspiciously, anxious, fidgeting and moving from cabin to cabin, but of course this can occur in many passengers who are nervous flyers. Very often other passengers would pick up on something they had seen and advise us that the passenger in a certain seat was acting very suspiciously and wanted to know if they had been thoroughly checked through security. Other passengers hear this conversation and it would make everyone nervous, when usually there is nothing to worry about.

However, the company wanted us to be fully aware of what might happen and how we could best prepare ourselves. It was extremely disconcerting to have these trained men screaming instructions at us and then being pushed to the floor. I was alright until we were blindfolded. This is a very strange feeling, as now I felt a lot more vulnerable, being steered through the cabin, that I knew so well, but not being able to see. Then to be told to lie on the floor and not to move, was actually very frightening.

We were told to try to keep a low profile, try and listen to what is being said between the terrorists, the more fuss you make the more likely you are to be in danger, so keep calm. Of course, as we well knew the flight crew would be aware of what was going on as this would hopefully be visible on their cameras and there was no way the flight deck door would be in any way ever to be opened, even with a gun pointed at our heads. This was an extremely daunting exercise but it did make us more aware about the need to be vigilant and a lot of the crew found it very upsetting.

It was not long after this that I had an incident on board that I felt needed careful handling. I noticed the passengers wandering up and down the aircraft visiting other friends in different cabins. This was not unusual but when I spoke to them and asked them to please take their seats they did seem extremely anxious and said they did not understand me.

They carried on talking in their own language, which is not unusual, but did not settle down and then their friends from the back suddenly appeared through the curtains, who had come to visit them. I thought I had better register this with my colleague that we should keep an eye on these passengers and during the meal service one of the men asked if I could help him fill out his landing card. I said I would assist him after the service, which I did, only to find they were all going out to America for helicopter training!

Later on when were going through Immigration in America, I saw that the Authorities had taken all these men aside and were holding them in a different room, and obviously were not at all happy with their explanations.

I often wondered what the outcome of this had been but of course could have been completely innocent, who knows.

I was even getting trips where I was working up the front in the premium cabins as some crew did not want to work there and as new crew were joining I was moving up the list so was not always at the bottom and therefore getting a choice of where on the aircraft I wanted to work. I knew from my first flight I would prefer to turn ' left' when I got on board as I liked the service better and I had my eye on being First Class trained after I had been flying for two years.

CHAPTER 27

The trips to Barbados were always very demanding and I cannot imagine over the years how many bottles of champagne and wine I have actually opened, a lot of which were on this flight. In fact, I have recently had physiotherapy on my right hand caused by the opening of so many champagne bottles and when I saw the Specialist, he said 'I have never before had to put on a patient's notes Injury caused by opening too many champagne bottles, this is certainly a first' he joked.

When we first arrived in Barbados, I saw the clear blue water beneath us as we came into land, the beautiful sandy beaches and best of all, the sunshine. The Caribbean destinations were always popular amongst crew when it was Winter at home and I could see why. As soon as I stepped off the aircraft the extreme heat hit me and I could not wait to get through the airport and get to the crew bus which would take us to our hotel.

The drive was amazing as we passed through the little villages where I saw locals cutting down the hands of bananas and on the beaches were colourful displays of handmade beachwear and jewellery. On arrival at our hotel, we were met by the sound of steel drums, cold towels and fresh lemonade for us as we were given the keys to our rooms. When I arrived in my room and opened the blinds the view from my balcony was stunning, I overlooked the beach and I could not wait to get out of my uniform and get into my swimming costume and go down for a swim.

There were two swimming pools and various beach bars where we had agreed we would meet for a drink later that evening. I could not wait to have a swim (me, who would have thought it) and as I had already met up with another member of the crew I felt much safer, however, I would still not be going out of my depth. Reading my book on a sunlounger sounds much more attractive I must say.

I sat on my balcony watching the sun go down before getting dressed and going down for a drink with my crew, although I knew I would not be staying into the early hours of the morning as I wanted to be up early for breakfast and back on my sunlounger for the day. On my way back to my room I ran into a crew member Jayne, who I had trained with, and we agreed to meet up for breakfast for a catchup.

I had by now got used to being away and sleeping in different hotel rooms and usually I was so tired, sleep came quite easily. The buffet breakfast was wonderful, a really good selection and would set me up for the day, although my friend Jayne had already been there for a night already so was flying home in the afternoon, as she had done the shuttle to Grenada the day before. It was a good chance to talk about how our first months had gone and although it was hard work and the tiredness was difficult to cope with, when you are sitting on the beach in Barbados it's unbelievable how lucky are we. I had to agree.

Jayne, like myself, had decided on a much smaller case than we had originally bought as the weight of the hardshell case, although strong, was so heavy to maneouvre in and out of the car, and on and off the baggage belts. The only time we took our bigger bags was when we were doing an American trip so that we would have room to pack our shopping, as it was two dollars to the pound at one stage, so shopping in America was cheap.

My next trip was Antigua with a shuttle to Tobago. I had managed to work out and make a list of everything I was always going to need to pack for a trip, depending on the destination involved. I always took my travel kettle as these were not always provided in the hotels, together with an adaptor, soft sock type slippers (got to have comfy feet as they suffer tremendously), tea, coffee, biscuits, crackers and cheese, unless it was a destination in America where I could buy any type of food as it was right on my doorstep. It was extremely difficult even for crew to take certain foods into America, even my milk, which I took on every trip, had to be longlife in a waxed carton and declared on my crew landing documentation. The American authorities were extremely strict, even with crew.

The temperatures in the different destinations changed the different items of clothing that I had to pack, ie. beachwear, suntan cream, insect repellent was a must as someone like myself would always get bitten alive as I have such pale skin. How come I would always make a point of spraying my whole body with suntan cream which was meant to be waterproof, together with repellent and the little devils always used to find the one missing spot, antihistamine tablets of course.

Of course, before I started flying I had to receive all my vaccinations which were recorded on a card and had to be kept up-to-date by crew, this was a Company regulation for our own safety and obviously, they did not want us to become ill down route. Unfortunately, illness down route was inevitable due to number of crew and some of the destinations we flew to.

It was mine and most of the crews worse nightmare to be stuck down route for days as the remainder of the crew would have to leave without you and depending on medical advice, you would be stuck in some hotel room until pronounced fit to fly home. In some places, the flights only went once or twice a week so you could be stranded there for sometime with only visits from hotel staff with your food for company. I always tried to take Vitamin C every day, both summer and winter, and I was extremely lucky not to have been ill, although had some near misses on the flight home when suddenly during the night, due to tiredness, a migraine might start or a cold or cough would become worse.

I had a friend who lived on my way home and if I developed a migraine I would stop at her house to use her toilet. However, sometimes to my horror, she would not be in and I would have to resort to her garden as I did not want to be sick in my car. She remarked one day 'for some reason she had a lovely patch of carrots growing in her garden'! Luckily she was a very good sympathetic friend, with a large garden, and the medication that I had been given by the Neurologist usually arrested the attacks. There were times I had left it too late to take the tablet.

I noticed on my roster that I had a standby block which proved extremely difficult for packing as when called by a bleeper from the Standby desk in my hotel room, I had to be packed and ready in uniform for the car to pick me up and take me out to the aircraft, or if time back to the airport. Standby crews were taken to a local hotel where we had to stay in our rooms for the allotted hours of standby, so this for instance might be 7 am until say 3 pm. You could be called for a flight at any time during this period but given 45 minutes to get ready as some crew would get into their 'jammies' especially if it was the Winter.

I found this very nerve-racking as for the three, maybe four days that we were on standby, it was to cover a crew member who had not turned up for the shift, or gone sick, so you could not make any arrangements for these days for fear you may get called. Sometimes in the last 45 minutes of the shift when I was thinking I was clear for the day and could go into town shopping, the bleeper would go and I would be off anywhere. There was just time to let JP and my children know where I was going to and when I would be back.

Even worse was the amount of clothing that had to be packed as it could be Kingston where it would be hot and I needed clothes for around the pool, or in the Winter JFK where it would be absolutely freezing and I needed my big furry winter coat, hat, gloves, scarf and boots for the snow. Spare uniform always had to be packed and suitable clothes for positioning back.

Positioning back meant that in the event of an aircraft going 'tech' the Company could only leave us down route for so long because we were needed back home, so we would be issued with Club tickets to actually fly home as passengers, which was absolutely wonderful and happened on quite a few occasions. We were not allowed to fly home in uniform otherwise passengers would not understand why we were not working, so suitable smart clothes was always to be taken in case this occurred.

I remember being in the Caribbean when some of the crew had forgotten this rule and when we arrived back in the airport we were met by the Managers to inspect us and they were not amused that some crew had returned in beachwear with flipflops and no ties!

It's strange how so many of the tips from other crew members came in handy when we stayed on an island like Antigua. More often than not, we had to pack up our rooms to do the shuttle flight to a smaller island and leave our bags in a secure area until we returned and were allocated another room, which I have to say was very tedious. These trips were often referred to as 'bed hopping' as there would always have been one crew down route, one crew brought the aircraft in from the UK whilst the crew who had been resting having brought the flight in the day before, would return to, say, Antigua, and take the passengers on to Tobago, for instance. This process was to stop crew from going out of flying hours, especially if there had been a delay in taking off from the home base.

However, we only had to take a small bag for the shuttle with a change of shoes and our onboard jackets, as mostly we would only be away for three or four hours. We would disembark the passengers travelling to Tobago, then sit in the aircraft on the tarmac and have our dinner, whilst the cleaners came on board. The aircraft would be stopping in Antigua to pick up passengers going home to the UK and my crew would be returning to our hotel to spend another night and then going home the following day.

This rotation all worked like clockwork until the aircraft went 'tech' in Tobago and the part had to be flown out from the UK, thus leaving us stuck in Tobago, where there are barely any shops to buy anything for the next few days. I was so glad I had been told to always make sure you pack a pair of flipflops, a teeshirt and shorts and spare underwear, washbag etc, in my shuttle bag. What a godsend, as I did not fancy staying for the next couple of nights with just what was given to passengers when their luggage did not arrive. Very little, a teeshirt that fitted all sizes! a few toiletries including a comb and toothbrush.

Luckily, I had imparted the above information to other crew and some had taken my advice. It was very hot and even the flat onboard shoes, together with the very fetching one size teeshirt was not the best for sitting around a hotel pool. My limited 100g suntan lotion and insect repellent had to stretch a long way as it had to be shared by most of the crew but it was really much like a big family when crew were away, we always tried to look out for one another.

121

When the Male flight was introduced, one of the best hotels and layovers, due to the aircraft going tech, was on the shuttle to Sri Lanka. We stayed in the most beautiful hotel, where my room was like a whole suite, for two days and nights and I was lucky a friend of mine was also on the same trip. The beaches were amazing, with fantastic food and the people were so kind and made us feel very welcome on this unscheduled trip. I was very sorry to leave and vowed it was one of the destinations that I would like to return to for a holiday.

CHAPTER 28

The first two years flew by, mostly because the roster consisted of six days on and three off. I was beginning to earn better money as the trips paid really well and it was better to be somewhere where there were little or no shops as the American trips were more tempting to spend money. I could have easily spent all the trip allowance on shopping so I had to limit myself very strictly. I was beginning to get on top of the debts I had been left with but the huge mortgage was an interest only and I knew I had to do something about this as when I retired I would still have this huge debt and no insurance to cover it.

Retirement, what was I thinking about, there was no way I could retire at whatever age I was and the Government had already told 'ladies of a certain age' we would not be getting our old age pension until we were much older. Anyway, I would need a lot more than my pension with the Airline and my 'OAP'. No, I would be joining the American Airline crews, who we used to meet in America where they were always allowed to go in front of us and we would stand chatting and I was amazed how many were well into their 80s. At this rate, I was definitely going to be the oldest airline crew member but as needs must I was not going to lose my house after all this.

My Manager called me into her office and I was trying to work out what I had done wrong, I had always banked the duty free money on returning to the UK, never took it home by mistake, made sure the alcohol bars that I was responsible for were all counted and locked for landing, not misbehaved down route (at least I could never be accused of being drunk as most people knew I was a teetotal, which was one good thing). It appeared I had been put forward to receive my First Class training, having completed my two years flying successfully. I was absolutely thrilled as it was something I had been wanting to do since I joined.

It was, however, explained to me that I would have to make a choice between this and becoming Purser, as usually, only two First Class trained crew and a Purser would be allocated on these particular flights. I would, therefore, have very little choice of position if the other crew member was more senior than myself and it would just leave me with, in other words, no choice. This did not deter me I had already decided on First Class and Purser might come later.

I had received quite a few commendations from members of the public about how they had enjoyed the onboard service and the attention I have given to them and making their trip so enjoyable. This really meant so much more to me than the letters from the Airline itself. This continued throughout my career and I still have a file of these, to me if I have made someone's journey a more pleasant experience or helped one of our older passengers out of their seat to go to the bathroom because they were afraid of moving, its all been worthwhile.

I received my date for First Class training which would last three days but this time I was so looking forward to training, as although there would be tests, it was all about the service, food and wines. The wines would be interesting as I could not imagine how I was going to cope with the wine tasting, which I soon realised everyone else was very much looking forward to.

The crew member who chose to work in the galley and was responsible for the food loading and preparation, was usually someone who had worked in this position for years and really enjoyed it. This person had very little contact with the passengers so it suited me to work out in the cabin where I was always happiest. However, the Purser always worked on aircraft left (which was the same side as the Captain) so I would be working aircraft right.

I would be responsible for four passengers next to the window and three passengers in the middle section. Very often couples would sit opposite each other in the middle section and would 'buddy dine' which meant one of them would move into the tiny seat opposite their partner, not the biggest or most comfortable of seats. However, I suppose it was more like sitting in a restaurant but with a very small seat and table. Many passengers, who had experienced 'buddy dining' decided to stay where they were to eat, enabling them to remain in their comfy seat, with their own table but still sitting next to each other.

First Class passengers could dine anytime they wished as long as there was enough time to complete the service and prepare for landing. The food came on board partly cooked and was put into the ovens by the crew member in charge of the galley. Likewise the preparation of the appetisers, starters, soups, salads, main courses, desserts, and cheese plates. This position was just like being in a restaurant, although if we ran short of anything, there was nowhere else to go for a top-up in the air! He or she, would set up the trolley by the aircraft door and we would run the service from there having taken the meal orders from the passengers and determining when they would like to eat.

I had already worked this out in my mind that the easiest way was to try and serve the passengers two at a time, starting from the front but of course like everything this might not work in reality, especially if couples wanted to buddy dine. The worse scenario would be if everyone wanted to eat at the same time, which very often happened at night due to passengers wanting to eat and then maximise their sleep if they had work the next morning.

Drinks were always served first, the finest Champagne and Wines were always loaded, different each month just to confuse us crew and we would need to be able to converse with the passengers as to which wines would be suitable for the food they had decided upon. This part was going to be difficult for me as I had not tasted alcohol for so many years and the thought of having to sample the wine now was something I am going to dread, much to the amusement of the others who could not wait to start the tasting - the best part of the training for some! Give me the food tasting any day, much more up my street, especially the desserts and cheese plates. I would have to watch my weight, otherwise, my onboard jacket would get even tighter and it was pretty snug already.

The Champagnes, the Red and White wines and the dessert wines were a great success with the others and it was just lucky we were starting in a hotel nearby and not driving home. However, of course like everything else, a test followed. We would need to know all about the different regions for wine growing, the grapes, the suitability for different foods and most important the 'legs'. I had often heard and seen people discussing the legs when drinking wine and I was about to find and how this was achieved.

Good thing we were wearing aprons as I could see how easy this process would be to swirl it around the glass and end up wearing it. We had to take the wine glass, add a small amount in the glass, then swirl the wine around and then watch as rivulets of the liquid formed like legs and ran down the inside of the glass. This was supposed to show how good the wines were and when it was explained how much each bottle cost, I would expect to see lots of legs!

However, I was going to make sure when on board not to pour too much in the glass because I could see we could all end up wearing the wine, especially on the beautiful white linen cloth and napkin.

The trainers laughed as they rarely had teetotals taking part in the wine tasting session, for most it was definitely the highlight of the day but at least I had a clear head for doing the test and with this knowledge, I felt I would be able to guide passengers without having to say I was teetotal when they asked for my recommendation.

All the glasses had to be delivered to the tables on a silver tray and then the chosen bottle of wine or champagne taken to the passenger, whereupon the label would be shown to make sure it was the correct choice, then a small amount poured into the glass for tasting. If suitable, it would be poured, obviously not to the top of the glass as we were advised that this was easier on the ground but in the air it would be another matter with the aircraft.

I passed the test with flying colours having tasted not a drop of alcohol, see it can be done.

Now onto the best part which is the preparation and tasting of the food. All the instructions for the presentation of the food were in the 'Chefs Chat' and the next part of the training was to produce potato quinnells, which was passing the potato between two spoons. This in many ways was the easy part, delivery of the warm bread rolls, between a spoon and fork was interesting. Many of the rolls went flying through the air, not a good look when undertaking a silver service delivery.

The tables all had to be laid in a standard way and if laying a table for a couple who were sitting in the middle seats, had to be laid in unison with the crew member opposite. Obviously, a lot of synchronization would be needed! So having liaised with your opposite crew member, the tablecloth would be laid, then back to the galley for collection of the silver tray whereupon the cutlery, not forgetting soup spoon if the soup was being taken, side plate with napkin and butter knife, water and wine glasses, salt and pepper. All to be laid in a clockwise rotation. On board we would liaise in the galley and then appear through the curtain of the aircraft at the same time, almost like synchronised swimming, but without the water, thank goodness.

Then back to the galley to open the chosen wines and the most challenging part, apart from the balancing of the wine glasses on the silver tray especially during turbulence, was as I said above, offering of the bread between the spoon and fork. I could see this would need practicing. At least with longhaul flights, there was plenty of time and no one was in any rush during the day, apart from businessmen who wanted to eat quickly so they could get on with their work.

I seemed to have mastered both of these roles but knew from the start I would enjoy being in the cabin better than being 'chief cook and bottle washer'. Of course, this was only the meal service, there was also the little question of the First Class washbags, sleeper suits, slippers and bedding.

With the meal service over it would be time to settle down for an afternoon siesta, so fluffy pillows had to be issued, together with a fluffy duvet which had to be made up by the crew member and sprayed with a lavender spray to aid restful sleep, usually when the passenger went to freshen up. On their return, the seat would have been turned into a flat bed and made up accordingly, as above, ready for an afternoon nap.

Cabin lights and window blinds would be lowered, unless specifically asked to be left up, and passengers would be left to sleep until afternoon tea would be served prior to landing.

I enjoyed the afternoon tea service as this was my favourite choice of meal. Table to be laid up in the same way but sandwiches, scone, jam and cream, cake, tea, including all types of speciality teas and champagne would complete this service. Throughout my time working in First Class, I campaigned for the return of the tiered cake plate but in all the years I was never successful and paper dollies were definitely out of the question. Too much extra to load I was told. How much extra room would two flat plates with the silver handle connections take, we could have got rid of some of the other more useless equipment.

I took my own dollies and crumb brush for the table but drew the line at taking tiered cake plates, so we were just given extra tea plates and silver cake slices, which they thought would placate me. Would this be good enough at the Ritz when afternoon tea was being served, I think not! After all I had conceded on the question of bone china cups!!!

As if anymore food would be required there was always to be snacks and if really desperate for more food the, Club Kitchen in the mid galley was always on hand.

I had managed to take this all 'on board' and we were able to practice with the food on one another which caused great hilarity as food was dropped and spilt but obviously would not be allowed in the final exam.

Just when I thought we were nearing the end of the course, there was the final stage which was the return journey home and the dreaded breakfast service, which I had convinced myself would be easy after the outbound service. How wrong could I have been.

On the night service, the First Class Lounge would be advised that the flight was boarding and it was always hoped that these passengers would be at the airport earlier and partake of the dining in the lounge. However, this was not always the case and they would leave the lounge quite late, arriving at their seats, whereupon we would then ask them whether they would be changing into a sleeper suit. Small, medium or large suits would be offered, together with slippers and their clothes would be hung in the wardrobe next to their seats ready for the morning.

Drinks of course, and passengers asked if they would be dining with us tonight. The trainers explained that some would just want hot chocolate and cookies, or the light meal, especially if they had already eaten in the lounge but others would not sleep and require the full meal. After take off all the seats would be laid flat into beds and need making up, unless the passengers were going to have dinner.

I was just thinking to myself this sounds very straight forward but by the look on the trainers faces I was sure there was a lot more to come. Of course, as I had been flying for over two years I was somewhat aware of certain elements of the night flight home.

However, the Breakfast service in First was a new experience. During the night we were busy carrying out the usual security checks, which would mean walking through the aircraft to see that all was well in each of the cabins, feeding the flight crew, then when the duty free puchases had been carried out and the trolleys returned, it would then be time for us to have something to eat. I have to say I rarely ate during the night flight home as eating at 2 or 3 Oclock in the morning did my stomach no favours. I usually bought something to eat in my hotel room before pick up and kept myself awake during the night with cups of tea, it did seem the brewer was constantly on as every time I checked with the flight crew they invariably asked if the kettle was on!

Once everyone had eaten, the amount of time that was left before landing was worked out, having deducted the time to carry out the breakfast service and the 40 minutes preparation for landing, the time left was divided into two. Certain working positions would mean crew would take first break and the second break would be the remaining crew, with five minutes in between for the handover. Throughout my flying days I always preferred to have second break as by then I was really tired and might get some sleep. It also meant that if I was lucky, the person who had been in the door rest area had made up a really good bed and all I had to do was open my precious sleeping bag and hot water bottle.

To keep ourselves awake, the liquor bags that each crew member was responsible for had to be counted as on arrival at base if a bar was found to be unlocked, or the paperwork not completed the person responsible would be in serious trouble.

The First Class bars were slightly different to those in the rest of the aircraft, as although we had a bar of miniatures, beers and mixers, the other bars held the expensive red and white wines, champagnes and brandy, together with full bottles of spirits and obviously counted in a different way. However, although these spirits could be left in the bar having been opened, the wines and champagne once opened had to be disposed of down the w.c. for landing. One of the bars held full bottles of whiskey, brandy, vodka, etc so therefore was counted differently. Again throughout my flying career I always made sure the last thing I did before leaving the aircraft was just to check all the bars had completed paperwork hanging on the outside of the door and was padlocked.

No one, however, is at their best in the very early mornings, even people like me who classed myself as a morning person, I have to say it was a struggle to get myself freshened up and looking 'bright eyed and bushy tailed'. My worst nightmare was an aircraft where the crew had bunk beds situated in the middle of the aircraft behind a locked door and up a very steep flight of stairs in the roof space. Contrary to what some passengers think the flight crew have their bunk rest area at the front of the aircraft, not in the same place as the cabin crew!

Many of the crew absolutely loved these rest areas, but they were very much like marmite, you either loved them or hated them. I was the latter as firstly negotiating the stairs in poor light was tricky, then finding a bed that was not already occupied and undressing without making a noise as some crew went to sleep immediately. Although I only took off my skirt so that it did not become too creased, whereas some crew actually got into their pj's. Having found an empty bed, trying to negotiate climbing into such a small space with my sleeping bag and then every time the person above you moved it felt as though they would be coming down on top of you. I can only say it was like, I would imagine, being entombed in a coffin and of course I could not put on the light to read as it would disturb everyone.

There were two seats at the top of the bunk stairs but again you could not have the light on and I always wanted to go to the toilet during the middle of my break, which meant negotiating the stairs so I felt much better in my bed made by the door, where I could read, turn the light off when I wanted to, go to the toilet, clean my teeth, do my hair and make-up before coming back on duty. When else would I ever get the opportunity of finding out what was going on in the celeb world of 'Hello' or 'Ok' magazines, which were always loaded with the newspapers and saved by crew to read during the night to help them keep awake, or read on crew rest.

However, I digress. The trainers explained that the best way to navigate through breakfast more easily was to ask the passengers if they wanted a full breakfast, which would mean waking them an hour before landing and thus losing valuable sleeping time, or 40 minutes to landing for a continental breakfast, more sleep, or leaving until the last minute about 30 minutes to landing whereby a cup of coffee would be given whilst sitting them up and whisking away their bedding.

Everyone has different ways of how they feel in the mornings and how they like to be woken up. Some passengers like to be woken up gently and have their breakfast, go to the washroom, wash and clean their teeth and change into their clothes. Others like to be advised when one of the two washrooms was free and will wait patiently, whilst others wake up at the last minute, grumble at the queue for the washroom and then hurriedly rush to change before the seatbelt sign comes on and then ask if there is any breakfast going!

All the duvets and pillows have to be stowed in a special bag ready for the cleaners to take away and be washed and it was no good trying to wrench these away from passengers who were still half asleep, it was best to wait until they were up and in the washroom. That was all very well but stuffing all this bedding into a rather small laundry bag in training seemed alright, but whether it would be the same on board,

I was yet to find out. All the breakfast crockery had to be collected in, of course most importantly not forgetting the flight crew breakfast dishes were to be cleared from the flight deck and the cabin prepared for landing. The liquor bars, which are not the same as in the remainder of the aircraft as they are the full sized bottles and therefore drinks have to be measured by ourselves, ie. singles and doubles, but still require paperwork and duty free paperwork had to be completed before all the bars are sealed ready to be taken away by customs.

I could see this was all going to need a lot of patience and organisation skills and of course co-operation from the passengers as not only was I going to be tired and sluggish, so were they.

Lastly, make sure we look as immaculate as when we came on board, smile and wish the First Class passengers, who must be allowed to leave the aircraft first, a safe journey home.

CHAPTER 29

Having passed the exam, I was now First Class trained and was presented with my First Class certificate, together with a booklet on how everyone from Royalty, Heads of State and the Church, Lords and Ladies, members of the Government, the list goes on, should be correctly addressed. It was an absolute godsend and I still have this booklet now. I could not wait to put all this information into practice, so no more turning right on the aircraft, I had worked my way up and from now on it was turning to the left for me.

Although I hoped that maybe my first flight might have a smaller amount of passengers so that I could take more time to get used to the exacting service. This was not to be as my first trip was a full Barbados but I suppose in at the deep end, perhaps the return journey might be quieter.

I was lucky that the Purser who was on the opposite side of the cabin just told me to watch and follow her which helped tremendously and the other crew member was a lovely part-time lady who had worked in that galley position for years and would point me in the right direction. Just trying to recall where everything went, and little things like always the bottle to the glass on the passengers tables is something I seemed to have a mental block over and there was the question of the delivery of the bread onto the plate and not into the passengers laps.

With the help of the other two crew, I thought it had all gone quite well and the passengers had been lovely, especially when I explained this was my first trip and as most of the passengers were couples I had to lay up the tables for 'buddy dining'. It was very squashed, not only on the little seat, but the table seemed particularly packed with crockery and glasses before the food had even been delivered. It was so lovely to hear from the passengers that it had been a wonderful flight.

This was to be one of many flights to Barbados and although I was tired, there I was, as I had been many times, sitting on my balcony overlooking this wonderful beach with its beautiful white sand and sparkling blue water lapping up on the shores which always looked so inviting. I would get up early the next morning, go down for breakfast and then I had earmarked a sunlounger which had my name on it, where tomorrow I would be sitting and reading my book.

The Caribbean is so beautiful to wake up to with the sound of the sea lapping up on the beach and the birds singing. I could not wait to take advantage of the sunshine as it was so cold at home. It always seemed so strange to think eight hours away we had been wearing winter clothes, now I was wearing my summer clothes and was going to lay on the beach and get a suntan, hopefully.

As planned, I was, having had a wonderful breakfast in the restaurant overlooking the bay with a couple of my colleagues, chatting over how the flight had gone and now laying on my sunlounger, how lucky was I. I might even be tempted to go for a swim as the water was so lovely and warm, although I still liked to feel my feet on the bottom and not going out of my depth.

Having spent all morning on the beach relaxing reading my book, one of the other crew came over and asked if I would like to go with them to the fish bar just outside the hotel. This fish bar is famous in Barbados and I could see why as the fish burger was absolutely delicious. It was then decided we would all meet up in the evening and the Captain had booked a table at a local restaurant enabling those who wanted to return to the hotel earlier could do so safely, whilst others could stay on much later.

Much later was not an option for me, as with all the lovely sunshine and the thought of going back on the beach early the next morning, a few of us decided to have our dinner and wander back to the hotel. It is amazing how tired you can feel doing nothing and the thought of staying out until the early hours of the morning and then staying in my room all the next day was such a waste.

On the way back to the hotel we decided we would meet for breakfast fairly early then catch the local bus into Bridgetown, the capital. The bus ride was an experience as the bus was quite small and very crowded, so we were glad that it was not too far to go as it was so hot.

Bridgetown was busy but very interesting. The size and number of cruise ships that were tied up in the quay were staggering as this destination was extremely popular with passengers who leave the ship and go exploring and, of course, more importantly shopping.

The cruise ships were extremely good for the economy of the country as the local people depend on these passengers buying all the beautiful crafts as gifts to take home as mementos, together with some exquisite jewellery. When you see these at close range the sheer vastness of these vessels made me wonder how they actually stayed afloat and the vast number of passengers pouring down the gangways is breathtaking.

Even more spectacular is when these huge ocean liners prepare to leave the bay, with all the passengers, hopefully, all back on board and the ship is ready to leave and they wait for no one. Passengers stand on their balconies and on deck and wave as the liner somehow with all that weight just gently glides, firstly outwards away from the dock, then majestically out into the sea and within minutes it seems to be miles away.

The best time to catch sight of these beautiful cruise ships I found was standing on my balcony watching the sun drop down, which happens very quickly, as one minute I was taking a picture, the next the sun had disappeared and in the distance there would be one of these liners gliding out to sea with all its lights blazing then suddenly gone and onto its next port of call. I keep being told by everyone how wonderful cruises are but I think its the fact they are out there most of the time in the middle of all that very deep water, that I still find a bit disconcerting. I have lost count how many times I have watched The Poseidon Adventure and Titanic, that's enough to put me off crusing! Maybe one day.

One of the girls on the crew decided she wanted to go and buy some jewellery as tanzanites were sold quite cheaply in Barbados due to the mines were becoming 'mined out' and therefore much scarcer to purchase. Some of the jewellery I have to say, especially the emeralds and tanzanites were beautiful and I promised myself if I ever got my finances back in order, I would come back and treat myself.

We were extremely lucky as there was no shuttle to one of the other islands such as Grenada, Tobago, Nevis and St. Kitts on this particular trip so we had the rest of the day to enjoy the beach before returning home the next day.

The flight home was very demanding and I think it was worse because we had time to relax for the past few days but now it was all systems go. As on all First Class night flights, all passengers would be offered pyjamas, small, medium or large and of course we had been taught to be very diplomatic in this respect. Most regular passengers did not care about the look but just being comfortable and would opt for the larger size. Others would squash themselves into a smaller size, which was a lot less comfortable for sleeping. Anyway, apart from crew, who was going to see them?

PJs and slippers were all handed to the passenger on a silver tray, and a glass of champagne offered to be waiting for them on their return from the washroom having changed and in the winter the wardrobes would be so full of coats it was sometimes like wrestling with a bear when the wardrobe door was opened. I would dread a passenger asking for his or her pen or passport out of their coat pocket which, of course, was right at the back of the cupboard.

Most people wanted to have as much sleep as possible, especially if they were going straight to work in the morning, so would opt for cookie and hot chocolate whilst others went for the full meal service. As soon as it was safe to do so when the seatbelt sign had been extinguished, there were beds to be made, although regular passengers would do this themselves. Within minutes, the eye masks were on, sleeping tablets were taken in some cases, the lights were dimmed and they would ask not to be woken until just before the 20 minutes to landing call, giving them time to change, and in many cases just in time for the seatbelt sign to illuminate.

It was much more difficult to carry out the dinner service with just the passengers reading lights guiding the safe passage of the food to the table but eventually, everyone had settled down, hopefully, for the night. Not until the meal service in all the other cabins had been completed, together with duty free, were the crew able to have their supper and prepare to have some rest themselves.

The rest period was split into two, one half going to rest whilst the other half made sure all was well in the cabin, making sure passengers had plenty of refreshments so they did not dehydrate and become unwell. A constant vigil and patrol were kept up during the night as that seemed to be, in many cases, when passengers became unwell. Flying, especially longhaul, takes its toll on the body, even for the fittest amongst us. People with underlying health problems, even just the stress of flying, can cause passengers to panic or faint and in the worse case scenario, to have symptoms of a stroke or angina attack.

Luckily we always carried a medical kit which every crew member knew where to locate, as if a medical emergency occurred at night it might be needed urgently as speed may be imperative.

Making a bed up by the aircraft door was just a matter of putting the two crew seats together, connecting them with a metal cannister, which was mighty cold if not covered with blankets. Some flights had no spare blankets as they had all been given out to passengers, or children who were cold, so it definitely helped to always have my own sleeping bag, together with my trusty hot water bottle, which came on every trip and was like a comfort blanket as it was so cold and draughty in the aircraft doorway. I became really proficient at making a comfortable bed, as I had been shown how to do this by a crew member who had been flying for years. It also helped to be just the right height to stretch between the two crew seats, being too small on this occasion was better than being too tall as some of the crew could not stretch out.

Sometimes if the breaks were short, I just managed to get settled and comfy in my made-up bed when it was time to change over with the other half of the crew. Certainly, I liked the second break as, having counted the drinks bars and done the paperwork, I was ready for my break, but I liked to be woken 10 minutes before breaks were over and breakfast started. I liked to make sure my hair and make-up were perfect, or as perfect as it could be at 4 am and definitely always cleaned my teeth, which usually woke me up.

From then on it was all systems go as breakfast was already in the ovens, including scrambled eggs. and it was just trying to wake passengers an hour before landing who had requested a full cooked breakfast. Some thought better of it and decided to sleep on, whilst others carried out their ablutions. I often wondered what passengers actually did in the washroom as some took so long and at busy times the queues for the two toilets seem to be endless and other passengers would complain. Sometimes I would knock on the door just to make sure the person was alright and they were quite oblivious to how long they were taking. It was like they thought they were at home in their own bathroom and were surprised when they came out and saw the queue.

Everyone, not only the crew, were not at their sunny best at this time of the morning but just getting a simple answer from a passenger was like pulling teeth. 'Good Morning Sir or Madam did you manage to get some sleep'. 'No, I did not sleep at all as there was too much noise'. Apart from crew working in First Class the remaining crew were not supposed to come through the First Class cabin and if necessary were told to be extremely quiet so as not to disturb the passengers.

'I am sorry you did not get any sleep' and it would turn out it was the noise from the engines and I knew he or she had slept, as when I was patrolling the cabin I could hear the snoring and definitely release of certain gases!

I always made sure I asked very simple questions that required a Yes or No answer and even that proved difficult for some passengers. 'Would you like to start with fruit or cereal' and the reply would be 'Yes', and likewise 'Would you like tea or coffee' and again the reply would be 'Yes'. I know it is difficult to get the brain into gear but surely a simple reply would do. Sometimes I wanted to bring fruit, cereal, tea and coffee to cover all requirements, it was like pulling teeth.

I had a system going, mainly to help myself for the last minute dash, whilst passengers were in the washroom I would put all their bedding into the laundry bags, clear their seating area, lay their table for breakfast so at least these passengers were ready almost for landing. Then came the light breakfast, tea or coffee, fruit juice and croissant. Not much laying up to do for these passengers but still bedding to be cleared away and some people would leave it until the last minute before trying to get into the queue for the toilets.

Whilst all the above was going on, I had to be mindful that I was responsible for making most of the personal annoucements on the aircraft. So I had to remember to listen out for when the flight crew gave the 40 minute call. Whatever I was doing, unless one of the other crew I was working with had time, the wake-up call to the whole of the aircraft had to be made. This was extremely daunting at first as it

135

was, in many ways, like being on stage as you could hear your own voice and it was so easy to make a mistake and give the incorrect information.

'Good Morning we hope you managed to get some sleep during this flight and as you have just heard from our Captain we have just 40 minutes to landing. The seatbelt sign will be switched on in approximately 20 minutes when the toilets will no longer be available so may I suggest you make use of this facility as soon as possible'. That twenty minutes used to pass by so quickly as there was so much preparation to do and it seemed within minutes the Captain, or First Officer, would be giving the 20 minute call. This would mean the washrooms would no longer be available and that all passengers should return to their seats and fasten their seatbelts ready for landing.

Sometimes it went relatively smoothly but I always marvelled at how in that short space of time we had all pulled together to help one another if one cabin was not quite ready, and we were all put away, bedding, crockery all stowed and we, the crew could pass the 'ready for landing' to the senior crew member.

It was nearly always a quicker flight on the return journey and we used to all guess how long the trip home would take. There were no prizes for getting the time correct but we were just pleased that it was usually quicker than on the outbound journey. It was just bliss sitting in my crew seat knowing that all I had to do now was read the landing PA which was easy on the way home as I was at home base at the time on my watch, unlike the outbound journey where I had to remember to work out how many hours difference the country we were landing in was. I remember in the early days starting the landing PA in the Caribbean and having to quickly work out how many hours ahead they were. If we got this PA wrong the passengers would be completely thrown and it would cause chaos.

I once advised passengers that the time in Antigua was four hours difference but we had changed our clocks at home and it was five hours difference. I soon had to do a retraction as people were altering their watches and of course, the locals knew I was wrong. I always made sure after that I checked the local time.

CHAPTER 30

I had some wonderful trips to Barbados and met one of my favourite celebrities in the whole of my working career and that was the lovely Sir Terry Wogan and his wife Lady Helen. Having nearly missed the flight as they were in the First Class Lounge, they apparently did not hear the final call. They were so apologetic, or rather Lady Helen was, Sir Terry just had me in fits of laughter as he was more worried about having to leave his drink.

Right from the word go he was just very natural, exactly as you see him on the television, extremely funny and he and his wife were an absolute pleasure to serve. This, I might say, was not always the case as some celebrities who appear to be lovely on TV were extremely precious and very difficult to please.

This was not the case in respect of the Dallas flight where I was lucky enough to have the opportunity of looking after George Michael, who was then travelling with Kenny Goss, on quite a few occasions. I always addressed the passengers by their surnames unless told otherwise but George Michael asked me to call him George. He was absolutely no trouble, he explained he was just going to have soup and then take some sleeping tablets so that he could get some sleep before arrival in Dallas, which although he had a property out there, immigration was always a difficult procedure. I was delighted that the person most people knew and loved was so thoughtful and kind, and on every trip we did together he always remembered me. I was extremely saddened to hear about his death, such a waste of an amazing talent. His signed autograph, together with an autograph from the lovely George Martin, Manager of the Beatles whom I am pleased to admit I was one of their most ardent fans, especially Paul McCartney, are amongst my treasured possessions.

If its any consolation to all the readers, I can tell you some of our most attractive ladies in the TV and Film world look exactly how we do when we first open our eyes in the morning and go to the bathroom, pretty disheveled. If they know they are likely to be recognised by anyone, but mostly the media, they would spend most of the landing time preparing themselves to be photographed.

I still think about this when I see 'stars' arriving on the TV and having a camera pushed in their face, I would hate to have anyone even see me, let alone take a photograph which will be splashed all over the front page of the newspaper. I know its the price you pay for fame but who looks good in the early hours of the morning having just done a longhaul flight, certainly not me.

We had, of course, many passengers who were real wine connoisseurs and even though I am a teetotal, I learned such a hugh amount about the different wines we served on board, especially as these were usually really expensive and changed every month to add variety for some passengers who flew on a regular basis with us.

However, on this particular day this gentleman, who was travelling with his girlfriend, decided to go through the whole wine list only to tell me that all the wines were well below standard and not fit to drink. He was, supposedly, a real authority on good wines but whether it was red or white nothing was good enough. Did I not have anything more palatable?

I returned to the galley and although I am usually very patient, of course, I realise these passengers have paid huge amounts of money and we want them to be happy with the product offered. However, he was so unpleasant and obviously trying to impress his girlfriend by saying the wine was just cheap 'plonk'. I had an idea and told the girls to empty two wine bottles and I would be back.

I then went to the back of the aircraft and asked the girls to give me three bottles of each of the cheaper wines, still very good but not the quality of the ones in First, put them in a duty free carrier bag and I then returned to the front of the aircraft. I then decanted these cheaper wines into the expensive bottles and then went back to the passenger and explained that I had searched through the wine racks and found three of this wine that he might find more suitable.

The other crew watched as I carried this cheaper wine out into the cabin, keeping a straight face, and served it to the passenger. To their amazement, but not to mine, the passenger said that at least some decent wine, this was just what he wanted and it was about time he and his girlfriend, who I am sure was quite happy with her first choice, could have a decent drink. He just hoped there would be sufficient for the whole of their journey to which I replied 'I am sure there will be as I will make sure they only had that particular wine', along with all the other passengers at the rear of the aircraft I was thinking to myself!

Still, we aim to please in any way we can with the limitations of being on an aircraft, although the airline rules were very strict about not mixing the products in the different cabins but sometimes if one cabin had something that another had run out of we had to improvise. To me it did not matter whether you were in Economy, Club or First, I always hoped that I could go that extra mile, which was one of the Company's important values to us, and make sure when all the passengers got off the aircraft they had received the sort of experience I would expect, whatever the cabin.

CHAPTER 31

I am always being asked, which was my favourite destination, and it would be an extremely difficult choice between the Maldives and Bermuda.

Bermuda was one of the shortest flights we were rostered, only approximately 7 hours, it paid the most in allowances and was, in my opinion, one of the most beautiful islands, very colonial and so pretty.

The drive from Bermuda airport to our hotel was stunning. There are very strict regulations, not only in respect of residency, but you must have been born in Bermuda or lived there for a period of 10 years and you are also restricted with the colours that you are allowed to paint your property. Pinks, greens, yellows and peach are the traditional colours, together with white roofs and most of the areas are immaculate with beautiful vibrant coloured flowers growing everywhere.

The hotel itself was right on the waters edge and 10 minutes walk from Hamilton, the Capital. If I was lucky enough to have a room facing the bay, the views were breathtaking of the yachts and cruise liners and there was a shuttle boat which would take us just across the water to the sister hotel where we had the use of the most wonderful spa. I was lucky enough to spend many happy hours there just either sitting on a sunlounger looking out to sea whilst having my lunch or tea served to me, or relaxing wallowing in the jacuzzi.

There were outside pools in both hotels but the spa had an inside pool, which I used when the weather was not so good as the temperature in Bermuda is very much like in the UK. Many of the new crew were unaware of this and thought it was more like the Caribbean but the temperature dipped in about October/November and just like the UK, a jacket or cardigan would be needed.

I used to walk into Hamilton for my breakfast as there was a restaurant I particularly liked that overlooked the bay and very often I would sit having my breakfast, reading my book and watching the cruise liners coming in or setting sail. It was always an interesting watch to see the majestic liners just gently floating away with such ease, although I guess there is alot of work involved in this precise manoeuvre.

It is far from cheap in Bermuda even the small Marks and Spencer was quite pricey but I was lucky enough to be able to shop in one of the oldest family stores, Trimminghams, founded in 1841 before it closed in July 2005. I managed to buy a Gucci watch for less than half price in their closing down sale and I still treasure this now as the memories come flooding back of my time spent there.

It was very colonial and it was strange to see the men going to work in places like Butterfields Bank, the oldest bank on the island, in their famous Bermuda shorts in varieties of lovely colours, together with matching long socks. I wondered if this tradition would catch on for our workers at home and I did suggest this to JP but he could not see himself turning up for work dressed in that way.

I took my daughter, Elizabeth, and my sister, Barbara, out to Bermuda on one of my trips and they absolutely loved the island and especially the spa. Elizabeth actually managed to swim with the dolphins when we visited the Royal Naval Dockyard, which was also a great place to see, full of the history of Bermuda.

A few years later we moved from the hotel in Hamilton across to the sister hotel whilst a refit took place and this meant that we were actually at the spa and unlike Hamilton which had the bay, this hotel had the beach. Together with the beautiful white sandy beach and the beautiful blue water, which I must say always seemed to be quite cold even on the hottest of days, was an ideal place for weddings. In fact, Elizabeth and I managed to gate-crash a wedding as we walked down to the beach in the evening and to our surprise we were handed a glass of champagne as they thought we were guests. Result in my daughter's eyes, beautiful beach and champagne, what could be better.

The breakfast at this hotel was amazing, all beautifully laid out in the old fashioned colonial style with the staff dressed to match. The crockery was beautiful and the crew used to tease me by saying this was right up my street and I longed to have one of the small silver butter dishes with a domed lid to grace my table at home, not that it would be appreciated by my children, they would just think I had lost the plot. What happened to the plastic butter tub I could hear them say, this does not hold much, won't even cover a slice of bread. I never did get a butter dish.

Of course, the breakfast had everything you could possibly wish for, a different freshly squeezed juice of the day, cereals, eggs made in every way possible, buffet cooked breakfast waffles with different varieties of fruits, cakes and pastries, a speciality table with something new every morning. So breakfast would take us two or three hours as different crew joined us and we stayed for more coffee.

I found out later that despite thinking fruit at breakfast was a good start to the day it was like 'the kiss of death' for someone like me who had suffered from an ulcer in my early twenties, so always had to be very careful of my diet from then on. I had, over my flying career, developed IBS, as many crew do, and the many indignities too many to elaborate on about having to find a toilet with all speed, even to the point of telling the ladies in front of me that I was pregnant in order to jump the queue as I was so desperate for the toilet. I must say they looked at my stomach very suspiciously, but women are having babies much later in life and the ladies in Bermuda were too nice to query the fact.

It was after this embarrassing episode I was explaining to my Doctor who suddenly asked if I always had a bowl of fruit for breakfast, only to be advised that this was making my IBS worse and there was me thinking I was being so healthy. It would have been nice to have been told this earlier as when I stopped all forms of fruit in the mornings when my stomach was empty, the IBS became so much better and in fact improved so much that I no longer needed medication. It was surprising how many people's IBS improved when I imparted this information.

There were a few little shops in the hotel and the shop where I used to buy items from a local artist, chopping boards with instructions on how to make banana bread and my most favourite was the Caribbean Rum cake which was also sold in banana flavour. I always bought this cake when in the Caribbean, or Jamaica or Bermuda as it was just absolutely the best. There was only one problem, it was delicious but not quite big enough.

I am never tired of going to this beautiful place, the people were so friendly but like every place we visited we were always advised to be careful and vigilant as there are dangers wherever we went, just like at home. Unfortunately as crew, sometimes we could become a target as we were seen regularly in these different resorts and I was aware we were very often being watched. We must have stuck out like a sore thumb for some reason. Any poor conduct would be reported back to the Airline Company and we would be reprimanded.

Some places we were rostered to fly to were more difficult than others to go out in once we had arrived at the hotel, so we would make the best of it and always arrange to meet and go out as a group. Wherever crew went, we had always been advised to be vigilant as the locals started to recognise us and we seemed to stick out like a big sore thumb. We were always being asked 'you are crew aren't you?'. Even to this day people still think of me as crew and even people who do not know me ask me this question, they say there is something about me, although I am not sure what.

One such visit was on a trip to Kingston when we went to Montego Bay for the day to see the falls. Needless to say, anything concerning water is always 'You go and climb down, I will look after the bags, cameras, mobile phones and I will see you at the bottom'. So much nicer to sit on the beautiful beach on my sunlounger and await their arrival.

I used my own counsel a great deal over the course of my flying

Mary Middleton

career, although not always successful but on this occasion, everyone was being persuaded at breakfast into taking the Company's catamaran out in Antigua to the island that was visible from the beach. Little islands from the beach do not look very far away until you start either swimming or taking a boat out to reach them.

I took up my position on my sunlounger on the beach in my usual place and watched as those that had been cajoled into going on this trip by one of the crew who was supposed to be an experienced sailor, was trying to push the catamaran out whilst everyone jumped on board. I watched for a while until they started to sail away then returned to reading my book. When I looked up they were a long way out having still not reached the island and then to my horror the catamaran tipped over and everyone was in the sea.

I just counted my blessings that I had stayed behind as now they were struggling to get the catamaran righted in the water as the sea was not as calm as it could have been and it was proving difficult. After watching for a while I felt I had to do something, so I went and asked one of the guys on the beach if he could take one of his jet bikes and ride out and go and see if they were alright.

Luckily all was well and with his help, they managed to get the catamaran the correct way up, climb back on board and return to the shore. The girls were less than impressed when they returned as this whole procedure had taken at least a couple of hours, and they had still not reached the island, which was quite a fair way off. Staying on the beach would have been alot more preferable they decided.

On the way over to Antigua, I had the pleasure of looking after a lovely couple who it turned out were flying out to Antigua to meet their boat/yacht, which had been in the UK having a refit and was being brought into English Harbour by their crew. The gentleman had just had a serious operation and his wife needed assistance to help him up to visit the toilet and it turned out she was running a helicopter company they owned and was a helicopter pilot herself.

Just before we were preparing to land and saying our goodbyes, he had booked wheelchair assistance and I was making sure all was in place, he asked if I would join them on their boat for lunch the next day. His wife explained they were so grateful and would be so pleased if I would agree to go and they would send one of their crew to collect me next morning. How could I refuse such a sweet couple?

The rest of the crew teased me on the hotel bus and said it was probably some small dingy, or a cabin cruise and they would probably take me away never to be seen again. I had to get permission from the Cabin Manager and let him know the passengers names and exactly where I was going just to be on the safe side.

A Longhaul To Success

The next morning I had time to think about it and was not sure I really ought to go but, heyho, maybe I was turning down a wonderful opportunity. So when on the dot of 11am the crew member, who was a girl called Annie, turned up and I was ready. When we reached the quay, Annie sent me down the jetty whilst she parked the car but of course I was not sure what I was actually looking for as I passed all these small cruisers expecting to see the couple. The only boat I could see was the huge super yacht at the very end of the jetty and I decided to go and ask someone in the office.

I was absolutely amazed when she said 'You cannot miss their yacht as its the boat right at the end of the jetty'. It was the super yacht. As I walked towards it I could not believe my eyes as it was absolutely enormous! Suddenly Annie caught up with me and the couple were welcoming me aboard this magnificent boat. It was like being welcomed aboard the Royal Yacht Britannia. I knew nothing about boats so I was not sure whether to call it a yacht, boat or a ship, was I going starboard or port. Even Mrs Bucket (Hyacinth Bouquet) would have been totally in awe of this magnificent, I will call it, yacht. Although I was glad I had, sort of, worn something blue and white luckily which looked fairly yacht worthy.

The crew had sailed the yacht up from Falmouth in the UK, after having undertaken some repairs in readiness for the trip, they were going to make all around the Caribbean. I understood the yacht was worth a very large amount of money and it certainly lived up to that figure and more.

I was welcomed on board and was offered drinks and coffee before lunch. I was then given a guided tour of the boat, the lounge and dining area were impressive and then when I made my way below to the bedrooms, they were equally as stunning with beautiful fabrics used for the bedspreads and curtains and bathrooms to die for. I was then taken to the crew's quarters and the kitchen, where everyone was busy preparing the lunch. It was amazing to see their kitchen compared with the galley we had to work in, all modcons, no expense spared and a larder that could be compared with any high class restaurant.

Having seen the lower deck it was time to see the upper decks and it had been decided that although the dining area had been set up inside, the weather was suitable to sit under the canopy outside and have lunch. If only JP, my friends and my crew could see me now, this was just the height of luxury and the couple were so appreciative of the help I had given them during their flight, they could not do enough to make me feel welcome.

The crew served a wonderful lunch and I could not believe how breathtaking it was to be sitting so high up on board this yacht and

143

watching everything that goes on in the busy English Harbour. The couple were so interesting and I heard all about their helicopter business and was amazed that the lady was actually a pilot. I always said it was amazing just what you learn from passengers if you take the time, and in some cases, have the time to enter into conversation with them.

Anyway, with lunch over, the gentleman wanted to show me the heart of this yacht which was the wheel and the instrumentation. In many ways it was similar to being on board an aircraft and I was totally in awe of how this huge boat could be manoeuvred in and out of the different harbours but it was all explained by the Captain.

I had the most wonderful day, everyone had been so lovely to me and spent so much time showing me around. My only regret was that I did not have a mobile phone with a camera in those days, unbelievably, and I had not taken my camera but it will remain as one of the highlights in my flying career.

I said my goodbyes and hoped I would welcome them on board on a future flight but in the meantime wished them a safe journey. I was taken back by Annie to my hotel where I found the crew sitting around the pool and when I relayed my story of my days outing to them, they were extremely jealous, especially with the wonderful food I had eaten, better than a five star restaurant at the hotel!

See, you never know who you might meet, or what the day might hold.

It was not long after this that I was told by my Son that his old school friend had been taking a course in how to crew one of these yachts and that was to be his new job and had actually been out in Antigua working. He really loved it and I could see why. Although I prefer my feet to be on terra ferma, as it would be just my luck to fall overboard.

CHAPTER 32

I remember being on the Orlando flight and this lovely older gentleman I noticed had been in his seat for much of the flight, so I asked him if he would like help to get to the toilet. He said 'he was afraid of falling so had not bothered to try and make it to the toilet'. I realised for so many people, walking around on the aircraft was not always easy and they need help but feel they cannot ask.

I helped him and during a conversation, I learned from him that he was going out to visit his son who was the signatory for Walt Disney. He showed me a very special watch he had been given and was obviously so proud of his son. During my flying career, I met many such people for some amazing stories to tell. I never knew who I would meet next, not just stars and personalities but sometimes just very ordinary people with an interesting story to tell.

It was also on the Orlando flight that I had an encounter with Hurricane Katrina. Whilst travelling outbound we had been made aware that the hurricane had devastated Orlando and we would be lucky if we were even allowed to land. However, luckily we were the only aircraft given permission to land and I have to say the whole experience can only be described as eerie. It was extremely strange not to see any other aircrafts landing. The passengers were offloaded and were not very happy as it seemed alot of the hotels were closed due to hurricane damage. We entered the customs hall and just as we prepared to show our passports, one of the staff came screaming 'get out the way! Luckily we never questioned them and just as we moved the ceiling came down and water poured through exactly where we had been standing. What a lucky escape but it really shook us up, but worse was to come.

The drive to our hotel was a very bizarre experience as there was a strange silence. However there was noise of the wind and rain, which had greatly subsided and the sirens of the emergency trucks going out to fallen debris. On arrival at the hotel it was almost in darkness as they were trying to work on an emergency generator but they were unable to produce any food apart from trying to get a bbq going. The Captain was asked if we wanted our own rooms or wanted to share, which was something we were not used to doing. However, some of the crew were really scared and were quite happy to share but there was the problem of the key cards to enter the rooms as they were not working. It was also suggested for safety reasons we might like to sleep in the bath just in case the glass from the huge windows shattered, or in fact in the hotel corridors.

It was all decided between the crew, the Captain and the First Officer, obviously, to have their own rooms as by now we just wanted to go to our rooms as it was really getting dark by now and I for one did not want to be wandering about in a huge hotel in the pitch black. However, as we entered the lift the key card closed the doors and started to move but then the lights went out and we were now stuck in the lift. Luckily we were able to ring reception but it was at least thirty minutes before the lift started to move again and then we had to wait for staff to come and open our rooms with the staff keys as the emergency generator could not cope.

We were so relieved to get into our rooms at last and although we were really hungry we decided not to chance going anywhere until morning when we would meet and all go to Target, who we understood had an emergency generator and would be open for breakfast. It is really surprising how many things you suddenly realise you cannot do without electricity, like boiling a kettle, ironing and even reading a book with a torch is not easy.

Having checked on the other crew some of whom were very anxious, I was glad to go to sleep but in the morning I woke up with a really bad headache, which I knew could turn into a migraine. We met up to make the short walk to Target hoping that their emergency generator was working and we could buy breakfast. Unfortunately, the damage to the car park was severe and although the emergency services were already hard at work, trying to restore things back to some normality seemed an impossible task.

The noise was deafening to me from all the equipment as my headache was really taking hold but we were all so delighted to find Target, in the midst of all the chaos, was open for breakfast. There was obviously a long queue, it was like I would imagine queuing for rationing would have looked like, as everyone was only allowed one item each. I had taken my special medication but all the noise and lack of food was making my headache worse but we were so delighted to have some kind of food. However, I only managed to keep mine down until we turned the corner on our way back to the hotel whereupon I was promptly sick, much to the other crew members horror. What a waste having waited so long but as people who suffer from migraine know that is how it sometimes goes.

At least the medication was beginning to work and I would be better ready to make the journey home and, so I thought, things could only get better, how wrong could I have been.

On our way home, the winds from Hurricane Ivan crossed those of Katrina and the next thing we knew the aircraft dropped and the trolley we had out in the cabin had hit the ceiling of the aircraft. I felt totally breathless and it appeared I had cracked two ribs, but even more painful, I had caught my right elbow on the passenger's seat as I fell to the floor. I had not realised how dangerous the cracked ribs were until the Medical team that we were always in contact with said I might have punctured my lungs.

It was more painful to sit down so we decided to carry on with the drinks service, even though I could not do up my gilet. I was amazed when a passenger said to my colleague 'I asked her for a gin and tonic ages ago and I am still waiting'. My colleague just replied 'had you not been aware that we had sustained injuries and my colleague had probably cracked her ribs', but he really seemed unconcerned as he was more worried about his drink, so we had obviously managed to keep everything under control, although passengers were shaken up by the incident.

On our arrival at Gatwick the aircraft was met by management and medics and everyone was assessed for severity of personal injuries. There was very little that can be done for my ribs, they had to be strapped up. My breathing was back to normal but believe it or not, my elbow was alot more painful and took longer to repair.

This is why it is of great importance to make sure seat belts are securing fastened and passengers with babies and small children should have seen what happened to us when they are asked to take their children off the floor and out of bassinets etc. when the seatbelt sign goes on and they start creating that their child has just gone to sleep. We realise how annoying this can be and do sympathise, as most of the crew have children, or had dealings with children, how dangerous this could be in the event of severe turbulence. Always remember that crew are asking you to do these things for your own safety and not just to be difficult, as they know what might happen in extreme circumstances, which luckily does not occur very often.

CHAPTER 33

Some of the crew really liked being down route in the Caribbean and seemed to be tanned all year round from lazing on the beach but as they say, you can have too much of a good thing. We were known as the 'beach fleet' and it was lovely to go somewhere sunny when it was cold in the UK but coming home took some getting used to as once we landed back home the cold would set in.

I could not wait to get off the crew bus and get into my car, which I always hoped would start as it had been sitting for sometimes up to five days, and I had put hot water in my hot water bottle prior to landing and would travel home with it on my lap. The heater in the car seemed to take forever to warm up and if the car had to be defrosted, or snow scrapped off, the tiredness of having been up all night working would set in and I could not wait until I turned the car into my driveway.

My Son used to say 'If you want to ask Mum anything that requires a 'yes' answer, ask her when she has just come in from a trip as he knew I would just say 'yes' as I was too tired to even think about entering into any form of conversation. Even stopping off on my way home to buy food, took me all my time to concentrate on and if given a choice of two I would have to buy both, as I would never be able to make a decision.

Some of the trips to places like Orlando and Tampa were amongst my favourite, as soon as we landed and arrived at the hotel I would be showered and straight out to the Mall for shopping. Despite being extremely tired it was no good laying down and going to sleep otherwise I would have been awake at 3 O'clock in the morning as there was usually a five hour difference between the time in America and ours.

The weather was usually warm and the shops in the Mall stayed open until 10pm so I would grab a salad from my favourite cafe, Panera, and then to one of the best shops in America, Bath and Body Works. This shop was famous with the crew for their beautiful candles, they are absolutely the best and together with their handwashes, smell absolutely wonderful. I spent many hours shopping, not only for myself but for friends and family, as once they tried anything from this shop, the orders came flooding in.

Likewise, Target was another favourite. Sometimes the crew would agree to meet up and it was like a pilgrimage to this shop which was like Asda or Tesco back home. Somehow Target and its sunonmous red and white plastic bags were a must and crew regularly were seen with lots of these and bath and body works bags on the crew bus. Sometimes it was difficult to manage all the goodies that had been purchased in the

US as the choice and rate of exchange was so good.

Despite all this, a trip to Target after a long busy flight was a must and very often what seemed a good idea the night before, once I woke up in the morning I could not believe what I had actually bought and have to make a return trip. It reminded me very much of an old store called Woolworths back at home in the 'old days' and together with the dollar store the bargains were amazing.

It was on one of these shopping expeditions in Orlando that I came out of T J Maxx and saw there was quite a crowd of people standing around outside and looking up. Now I never wanted to ever miss anything in life so I too decided to stand with them and look up, although not sure what I was about to witness, when to my absolute amazement everyone shrieked with delight as one of the space shuttles was launched from Nasa's Kennedy Space Centre, it was truly breathtaking.

JP and I had already been to the Nasa Space Centre when we were in Houston and we were able to see where and how the astronauts were trained. We were also allowed to see the old command centre which had been left exactly as it was.

I always woke up early as my body had not quite worked out the time difference so I would get up and go to Paneras where I could order a cappuccino in a huge white china cup, and a cinnamon bagel with raspberry cream cheese. I am, if nothing else, a creature of habit and I used to take my order and go and sit outside in the sun and read my book and watch the world go by. Very often other crew members who had also woken up early would join me on their way to Target.

For lunch, I would return to Paneras for a bowl of brocolli cheddar soup and a salad before returning to my hotel room to try and get some sleep before pick-up.

I think during my flying career I could have had shares in Paneras, Target and Bath and Body Works, where in some places I was actually welcomed by first name terms, which was a bit worrying.

Getting on and off the crew bus always proved quite challenging as any shopping, that did not fit into suitcases, had to be carried as well as our large suitcases, which always weighed a ton, and a wheelie. However, we somehow always met the challenge and I became really good at packing. It is amazing just how much one suitcase and a wheelie would hold. Having got them from the bus it was then being able to heave them into the boot of my car and in all the years I flew I only ever had one broken candle and one handwash deposit itself all inside my suitcase, which was not bad. I was even persuaded by another crew member who was just as adept to shopping as myself, to buy a marble waste bin for my bathroom which weighed a ton and I managed to get it home all in one piece. It seemed a good idea at the time along with her buying two giant dog beds, which of course she could not buy at home!

Birthdays and Christmas were easy present wise, everyone just wanted Bath and Body Works products but I ended up doing all of my friends and family's Christmas shopping, the list was endless. At this particular time, crew were always desperate to get a US trip so that they could do their shopping and the Caribbean was no longer top of the list.

Christmas in Florida was out of this world but it felt strange to be Christmas shopping with Santa in the Mall as we were dressed in summer clothes. It always seemed more like home, especially in places like New York where the winters were bitterly cold. To see the shops all decorated and the tree in the Rockefeller Centre with the ice skating rink in front was always a beautiful sight.

It may seem crazy after a long tiring flight but the topic of conversation on the crew bus was whether we would make it in time to get to Bath and Body Works in the nearby Mall before they closed at 9 pm, as very often the deals on candles ended that night. They opened at 8 am but during the night the deals would be changed and because crew were such good customers, if we were there on the door next morning they would honour the deals we wanted. How sad were we, but I do miss the shopping and the lovely people in the shops that made us so welcome.

CHAPTER 34

My girls, having flown the nest, left my Son and I. I knew eventually the house would have to be sold as I was only really just keeping my head above water in respect of the mortgage. I was earning really good money with the trips I was rostered but I realised I was not moving on in my homelife.

It takes a long time to learn to trust again and you know you have to move on with your life, otherwise you will be stuck in a rut and feel you will never be able to make that final move for fear of the outcome. There was a whole world out there that I was managing to explore and be part of and with my travel concessions, I could take the family and JP with me instead of just standing looking at these wonderful places on my own. Would I ever feel able to negotiate through the muddy waters until I felt safe and at ease again?

This was our family home and of course, no one wanted me to sell it, especially my Son. I spent many sleepless nights trying to work out how I could make the huge debt I had been left with go away. I had managed to pay off the loan I had secured to pay the school fees which was something. I knew, just like the girls, Max would at any time decide to also fly the nest but at the moment moving seemed out of the question. Maybe if I could hang on and wait for the right time to sell up and move on, although the house still needed alot of work, so that I could raise enough money and did not become the eldest cabin crew member on the payroll.

Unfortunately, this was my problem, I just seemed unable to make any positive decisions when it came to my future life but with being away a great deal of the time, I suppose I always put this on the back burner, but it was not going to go away. Once your credit rating is damaged, it is extremely difficult to get it reinstated and bankruptcy was not an option as I would definitely have lost the house. It was going to take a leap of faith, or a miracle and I am not sure how many of those I have left.

Onwards and upwards, two new destinations came onto the fleet, St Lucia and Mauritius, and I had been rostered both. I was not keen on St. Lucia for quite a few reasons, I am not overkeen on horses being ridden up and down the beach at great speed and then being taken into the water where I am just about to paddle! Not sure just what was floating by but I had a good idea!

One morning I was dozing quietly on the beach when all of a sudden a very dark cloud appeared to obscure the sun. When I opened my eyes I found this was due to this huge black stallion horse rearing up right in front of me and the rider asking if I would like to go for a ride. As I was picking myself off the beach, having fallen out of my comfy sunlounger, I told him that horses and I did not go together unless they are behind a fence and I can safely pat them on the head.

There was also the long journey from the aircraft to the hotel, which took at least one hour, along very winding bumpy roads and being very hot in the crew bus, many of the staff became travel sick. I would always take sick bags off the aircraft, otherwise we would have to keep stopping to let them off the bus as the crew became so sick. This meant that the journey would take even longer and to make matters worse we had a days rest before we had to take the same one hour bus journey back to the aircraft and work the shuttle to Grenada, which only took 55mins, then make the one hour journey back to our hotel.

The flying time was nothing compared to the amount of time we spent on the crew transport. The hotels were only a short distance away and usually not airport hotels as they were felt to be too noisy.

The first hotel we stayed at in St. Lucia was completely different to any other we had ever stayed in, it was a series of apartments and for the first time we were required to share with other crew members, which we had not been used to. Each apartment had two bedrooms, shared kitchens and bathroom and the best part was out in the garden where there was a jacuzzi. Most crew did not like the idea of sharing as, like all jobs, you might be working with a person but you do not necessarily want to spend your down time with them as you might not get on.

A really good friend of mine had already text me to see if I wanted to share an apartment with him and I jumped at the chance to not only catch up but we had shared quite a few flights and shopping expeditions, so I knew this would work. This is what most crew tried to arrange before the flight so that everyone knew what they were doing and could arrange to take food as sometimes we would meet up in one apartment and that crew member would cook for a group of us.

Luckily, this had already been agreed but when my friend and I went to use the cooker it would not work. We tried desperately to light the flame but nothing happened so I decided to investigate further and found that the underneath of the cooker hob was full of water. On further investigation, it appeared that the apartment had been flooded during a very heavy tropical storm and when we checked the jacuzzi that did not look too clean either.

Cooking was out for us so we had to rely on other crew and there was an apartment restaurant where we could purchase food but we were promised we would be moved to another apartment on our return from the shuttle flight. Everything was going to be handled for us whilst we were away, all we had to do was pack our suitcases and leave them in our apartment.

As promised our luggage had been moved to a beautiful apartment overlooking the pool and as we entered the property we thought this was going to be a big improvement. As we had just carried out the shuttle service, my friend decided he was going to unpack and have a shower, whilst I decided, in my usual fashion, to put the kettle on for a cup of tea. I moved the kettle to fill it with water when it disturbed a nest of flying cockroaches, which had now become airborne.

For some insane reason, I decided to spray them with Fly and Mosquito spray which sent them into a frenzy, just as my friend had come into the kitchen/diner in his boxer shorts with wet hair which he was drying with a towel. When he looked up he went into a screaming fit and ran back to his room. I had, by this time, telephoned the front desk and they said 'they would send the maintenance man in a golf buggy to see what he could do and to stay calm'.

I was still in my uniform but as the maintenance man arrived, the sight that met him was my colleague running down the corridor still in his boxer shorts but with his uniform jacket and tie on, flipflops and clutching his suitcase with the contents of which was spilling out all over the floor whilst screaming. He was definitely not staying a moment longer in this apartment. He looked like something out of a 'Charlie's Aunt' race, I did not know whether to laugh or cry, neither did the maintenance man as my colleague rushed by him followed by some of the cockroaches and became firmly ensconced on the golf buggy.

It was like taking part in a pantomime farce! I had to collect my suitcase, which thankfully I had not even unpacked and because all the other apartments were full, we had no choice but to return to our old apartment. To compensate us, we had all our meals cooked by the restaurant.

We moved hotels shortly after this to another hotel much nearer to the airport, so that the drive and the shuttle would not be a problem but it was never a favourite of mine if I was being really honest and picky.

Whilst on one of these trips to St Lucia, the crew were meeting in the bar and there in front of us, with all her staff, was Amy Winehouse. She was very friendly and bought everyone drinks and seemed to enjoy our company as she had been staying in her own villa for some weeks. I was extremely sad to hear about her death and it makes you realise the pressures that these stars are under from the media.

Mauritius was a different matter, the hotel was absolutely amazing. I have to say most of our hotels were and it was quite usual during the flight that the crew would make arrangements for a trip out on our days off down route. One of the crew wanted to go to the Zoo in Mauritius but the remaining crew were not that keen as they wanted to sunbathe on one of the beautiful beaches.

Having said 'I would think about it', myself and another crew member found ourselves being persuaded to go to the bus station and catch a local bus to the Zoo to feed the lions. This was the first we had heard about feeding the lions but I felt sorry that she would have to go on her own, so we reluctantly agreed. I mean this was a tourist attraction so it had to be pretty safe and I had not heard of anyone being eaten, as yet.

Just catching the bus and making the driver understand was fairly difficult as the bus was not going all the way to the Zoo, it turned off beforehand and went on to the beach. We paid the fare and the driver did actually remember to let us know when it was time to get out at the bus stop and gave us instructions to get to the zoo, which I have to say I did not understand.

It was boiling hot and we waited over 30 minutes for the bus that would take us to the Zoo but when we got on the bus the driver looked somewhat bewildered and the fare was so small it obviously was not that far. I also asked him to let us know when it was time to get off and imagine my surprise and his when we went just over the brow of the hill, I had not even sat down before he told us we were at 'Zoo'. We had been standing in that heat when we could have walked from the bus stop in under five minutes, no wonder everyone looked at us as if we were mad.

Worse was to come. As we entered the Zoo, we were asked what tickets we would like to buy and it was decided, much to myself and the other crew member feeling very reluctant, that we were only here once, we should take this opportunity of either feeding or walking with the lions. How dangerous could this be? We were soon to find out.

At a set time we arrived at the lion enclosure and were greeted by the Lion Keepers and we were asked to sign a disclaimer should anything untoward happen. Untoward, what did that exactly mean, I just thought they were joking as we would just be pushing meat through the bars.

My friend and I were becoming extremely nervous and I had visions of being on the front page of the paper,' Cabin Crew eaten by lions in Mauritius' but I still could not believe we would actually be going into the lion's enclosure. The door was opened and the eight of us went through to where the lions were laying, we were told not to make any sudden moves. What sudden moves, I was frozen with fear to the spot, the only move I was going to make was back outside, but it was too late.

We were given very strict safety instructions on how we must approach the one year old lion cubs, whose paws looked mighty big to me, very quietly and calmly and must hold the stick we were given should they get too near. Evidently, the lions respect the stick, stand your ground and never run or turn our backs. Get too near, they must be joking, I could not believe that I had signed a disclaimer and was now in the lions cage, this was pure madness and what was I thinking of when I agreed to this.

My work colleague, who suggested we make this insane venture, was overcome with excitement and kept saying 'Isn't this the best time ever'. 'No' I kept telling her, we were supposed to keep very quiet and not make any sudden movements, as she was jumping around all over the place like a child in a sweet shop. I could only assume she had led a very sheltered life, or just wanted to end it all, but the last thing I wanted to do was end my days being eaten by a lion.

The other crew member and myself were keeping well back and once the lion cubs, which seemed pretty big to me for only a year old, had settled down, we were told to move forward one at a time and we could give them some food and have a photo taken at the same time. I was not taking my eyes off the lion to smile at any camera! I was busy watching the others wandering around and I was holding the stick very tightly, that to me looked more like a twig and was not going to fend off any lion who saw me as his next meal.

Now, these lions that were the size of a large dog, had settled and we could move forward and stroke them. As if my shaking hand was not a give away, the Lion Keeper told us not to show any fear - 'Yes right, I don't think so'. As the lions were now getting more restless we were told that it was time to go. I thanked the Lord for letting me live.

When we eventually came out of the cage and saw the lions behind the bars of the cage I had to admit they were beautiful animals but better behind bars at a safe distance. I could not imagine how I had ever been persuaded to do this but our crew friend was so excited and could not wait to see her picture. Myself and my other colleague's photo looked exactly how we felt, patting the paw with the look of 'what am I doing' written all over our faces.

As if this was not the highlight of the visit, we had to then climb aboard the safari truck and drive around the whole park. Luckily I decided to take the inside seats as the next thing we knew the Emus were racing up the side of the truck, leaning in and pecking everyone. They can be really vicious and their beady eyes and sharp beaks were soon attacking those in the open sides of the truck and I ended up on the floor with my two work colleagues on top of me trying to get away from these horrible birds. It was like watching Rod Hull with Emu on the Michael Parkinson show all over again.

Once the safari was over and we managed to be able to walk around on our own, the massive tortoises that were big enough for an adult to ride on, although of course not allowed, were amazing creatures and the remainder of the park was beautiful.

The bus back to the hotel was less adventurous, I was just looking forward to soaking in my luxurious hotel bath as I was filthy and covered in dust. I looked on in amusement as the crew member who had suggested this trip, was still going on to the other girl about her wonderful day, but I could see from her face that she felt like me, could not wait to get back for a bath and was grateful to be in one piece.

I could only look at my photo with amazement and it was the only proof we had when we reached our hotel and showed the other crew what had actually happened on our trip to the Zoo, needless to say, they had all been lying on the beach.

I heard a few years later that a Lion Keeper and a tourist had in fact been attacked whilst walking and petting the lions and it appears that lions do not like being petted, as they would not have this type of contact with humans in the wild.

CHAPTER 35

Of course in my life, just when everything is going smoothly, I was so happy in my longhaul flying career and my homelife had reached a stage of stability, I might have known that something would come along to change it all.

There had been talk for sometime that the fleet would be amalgamating longhaul with shorthaul and suddenly it became a reality. We, as longhaul crew had mostly flown on longer trips firstly on the 747 before they had all been sent to Heathrow and we were then transported from Gatwick to Heathrow to operate them. Then on the 777. Likewise, shorthaul crews were used to shorter trips to Europe and Domestic flights, such as Manchester, Edinburgh etc. To combine the two fleets together was going to be challenging for all concerned. Those who were eligible went to Heathrow on a permanent basis, whilst others of us had to remain on the dual fleet.

I was extremely disappointed to find that, once again, I was eliminated from staying with my longhaul colleagues and going to Heathrow because of my age. longhaul retirement age was at that time 55 but the rules if this respect were due to change on the 1st April, making it unlawful to make someone retire as it was deemed to be ageist.

When I joined the Company I realised the rules were due to change and therefore, the fact I was due to be 55 in the June, I would be alright. I might have known that the Government would change the date for the ageist bill and move it to 1st October, which would mean I, like many others of 55, would be affected by this and lose out. I blame my Mother for not having had the foresight to have me later.

I really loved being crew on the Longhaul fleet, I had achieved so much and was really good at my job, even if I do say so myself, had given so much and it caused me great sadness when I and five other crew in the same age group, had our longhaul contracts taken away. We did try and fight our cause but no one listened and we were given a new mixed fleet, shorthaul and longhaul combined contract, but the Company did agree we could keep our staff travel and more importantly our original date of joining, otherwise we would have been starting from the beginning in respect of seniority. It was extremely hard to take and we found it very hard not to be bitter as the company would need our experience of longhaul in the coming months.

It also meant taking SEP training on the 737 for myself and the 777 for shorthaul crew. It took sometime before I was comfortable working on the much smaller aircraft with only one aisle and likewise for the shorthaul crew who had to get used to working on a much larger aircraft and staying away for longer periods of time. We all had our comfort zones and mine was definitely not shorthaul, luckily because there were so few of us left from the longhaul fleet I spent a great deal of time on the 777 helping out, which suited me.

However, the day of reckoning soon caught up with me, as I needed to be in recency with my 737 licence so I had to make a trip within so many days of my training. When I looked at my roster, my first trip on a 737 was the Jersey flight, which was from the sublime to the ridiculous as the amount of flying time was approximately 25 minutes in which time the whole service had to be carried out. I was not used to even getting out of my crew seat for the first 10 to 15 minutes, this flight was right out of my comfort zone.

Shorthaul days and trips could be even longer than a longhaul flight and believe me just as arduous with the number of turnrounds. For instance, the first day could be a Gatwick to Jersey, Jersey back to Gatwick, then returning to Jersey for a nightstop and early flight out next morning back to Gatwick. We would wait for maybe a couple of hours to take the, say Tirana, which was nearly three hours each way, so by the time we had landed, turned the aircraft around and boarded the return passengers we could work as much as a 12 hour day.

Believe me when I say I never realised how much more tiring shorthaul was, as with longhaul the passengers just board and we and they get off at the destination and stay overnight. This was a completely different 'ball game' as it was never ending welcoming passengers on board, which to me was the best part, saying goodbye, then doing the same thing for the return, visiting many lovely destinations but only as far as the tarmac as there were very few stopovers. On a shorthaul week I was using alot more fuel so it was lucky I had changed my car for a diesel model.

I arrived at the Jersey briefing and luckily I was just on this flight to assist and would not be counted, although there was so little room for everyone and nowhere to put anything. It was decided I would help out in Club where it was explained a full continental, or full cooked breakfast would be served in the short flying time.

The crew at the rear of the aircraft were responsible for the service at the back and would read the safety demonstration. That was my first experience of having to carry this out in a very long time, as most safety demos on longhaul are done by the automatic system.

It seemed as soon as the aircraft wheels left the ground and with the aircraft still climbing the bing-bong from the flight crew gave us the all clear to leave our seats and start moving around. What happened after that was a complete whirlwind, as passengers were asked whether they wanted a cooked breakfast or continential. How passengers ate a full breakfast with fruit juice, yoghurt, tea or coffee and were ready on the 10 mins call to fasten seat belts was miraculous and obviously they were used to this flight and had become quite expert.

I, obviously was not such an expert it seemed to be, I was handing out breakfasts and the moment the last mouthful of food was eaten by the passenger, the tray was whisked away. I understood why passengers who had experienced this flight on a regular basis decided just to have tea or coffee and for those who were using this service for the first time were as bewildered as myself. One lady asked me if she could have her coffee later and I had to explain to her that she would be having this on the tarmac as we were due to land in 10mins.

The Captain knew I was from the longhaul and was used to having the 40 minute call to prepare for landing, so he jokingly called me before we took off just to make me feel at home, as the whole flight to Jersey takes less than 40 minutes. The only trouble was having landed in Jersey we then would fly directly back to Gatwick, then back to Jersey for a nightstop. Jersey was probably one of my favourite domestic shorthaul flights as the hotel was lovely, overlooking the bay in St. Helier, and it was so easy to take a bus around the beautiful island and see the wonderful sandy beaches.

The shorthaul crew found the longhaul trips just as daunting and it proved extremely difficult for the crew who had children to arrange childcare, as the trips could be up to five days or more.

The arrangements for standby also changed for the worse, instead of going to the nearby Hotel to standby and wait to be called, we had to wait in the crew airport lounge in a chair, whilst still appearing immaculate if called to do a flight. This could mean 5 minutes into the shift, immaculate, or 15 minutes from the end of an 8 hour shift, pretty scruffy.

Its the closest I have ever come to a grown woman crying to think in 15 minutes I would be on the crew bus, going to the car park and going home only to hear the bing bong 'Would cabin crew (name) report to the front desk'. Everyone knew this would be to take a flight to anywhere and maybe for as many days as the standby was rostered, or just a shorthaul trip arriving back late at night. It was the dread of most cabin crew, as it was something we were not actually ever prepared for unlike a proper rostered trip.

However, one stroke of luck was to arrive at the airport for a standby block to find that a whole crew from our base was to be taken to Heathrow where we would be flying to Toronto for a nightstop. What a wonderful result and on the crew bus there was great excitment over this trip as quite a few of us wanted to visit Niagara Falls.

Having arrived in Toronto it was arranged that we would have to leave early on the 6 am bus as our flight was returning that night. As usual crew were, if nothing else, resourceful so we had planned all the timings, including the boat ride and we would even still have time for a quick trip round the shops.

We met at 5.45am to catch the bus which was fine as we could continue sleeping and the journey would take over an hour. On arrival at the falls we booked our tickets on the Maid of the Mist and then proceeded to cover ourselves with the red waterproof (so called) ponchos, as we knew this experience was going to be very wet.

For someone who does not like water, the whole trip was absolutely amazing, to be so close to that volume of water and the noise was deafening but it was absolutely thrilling. As the boat turned and we were virtually under the falls, everyone became extremely wet just from the spray but I would not have missed it for the world. When I looked at the pictures we looked like drowned rats, we were absolutely soaked. It was one of my most momentos trips and I would love to return and walk under the falls next time, believe it or not!

Some new trips were better than others and as long as it was longhaul I really did not mind, but this particular day I had arrived at the base for a five day standby block, which could mean five or more shorthaul trips. As soon as I arrived at the standby desk I was told to go and put my bags down the luggage belt as soon as possible as I had been selected to fly to Cancun. What a result as having looked at my briefing paperwork I was flying with a friend of mine, who was the Cabin Manager and this trip would take up my whole standby block.

The hotel was absolutely beautiful and my friend and I arranged to go down to the beach as we had heard that they were due to release the baby turtles as they were about to make their way safely from their nest to the water's edge. This was an extremely dangerous time for these little creatures and to prevent many of them from not making it, they received help at certain crucial times from trained locals and I was so pleased that I was able to help and watch them swim away and witness this amazing procedure.

Not sure about the armoured vehicles going up and down the beach which came as rather a surprise and was rather unnerving when I was laying on my sunlounger reading a book. Evidently, there had been a shooting just outside our hotel a few days prior and the troops were there for our safety! Not one of the places I would be eager to return to.

We also gained the Oakland route in San Francisco which I managed to get from a standby call, whereby a crew member was late for the briefing, as sometimes happened with the many hold-ups on the M25.

This was a real result as I had the correct clothing and although it was December, San Francisco was not that cold. It was, as was very often the case with the crew, decided on the crew bus that four of us would catch the early morning coach and take the boat over to Alcatraz the next day.

As usual, we were up early and reception advised that we needed to book our tickets as the visits were always pretty full. We were so glad we took this advice as we might have missed this trip and the guided tour, which was so interesting, even seeing the Golden Gate Bridge sparkling in the sunshine was magnificent.

When the boat arrived at Alcatraz it was not as I had imagined it would be, I never realised when it was occupied it was like a whole village on the island where wardens and their families actually lived. The tour was done by a headset pre-recorded tape which meant there was plenty of time to look around the whole prison at our leisure. It was hard to imagine the prison when it was full of the 1500 prisoners and how treacherous it must have been for those who did try and make their escape, due to the dangerous icy waters, with strong currents and sharks to contend with. Over the 100 years, only four attempts were successful, three of whom were never found so it was never concluded whether or not they had actually survived and one was apprehended collapsed from exhaustion.

I was now standing in one of the cells that would have been home to some of the most notorious inmates such as Al Capone, Robert Stroud, known as the Birdman of Alcatraz and was the most violent inmate and spent most of his time segregated from the other prisoners, and George 'Machine Gun' Kelly to name but a few, it was quite chilling.

We finished our tour via the shop and one of the inmates 1259 William G. Baker who had been a prisoner at Alcatraz since the age of 23 until his release in 2012 was there. Although Alcatraz was closed in 1963 and he was now 80. He had written a book on his time in the prison and was there in person that day in 2017 signing copies. His crime was to do with robbery and several unsuccessful attempts at escape from other prisons, and although I do not condone his crime, I was interested to read about his time in Alcatraz, as he was one of the last surviving inmates of the prison. He signed the book for me and strangely we had our photos taken with him, not sure why, but as I looked at this now, elderly man, I wondered whether it had been worth being incarcerated for most of his life. He died in July 2020.

The Vegas trips were great fun and I took JP on one of these trips, although we were not very good on the machines and tables, we went to see a show on the strip and had breakfast at the Venetian Hotel. The fountain show at night from the Bellagio Hotel was amazing and everyone would wait just so they could catch this nightly extravaganza.

Mary Middleton

In fact, the whole of Vegas was very noisy and glitzy, I went several times but have no real desire to revisit, although I do know many people who love it for the gambling and go every year. My daughter, Elizabeth and her husband loved it in Vegas and were very lucky on the tables but I have to say JP and I never made our fortune.

We also took on the flight to the Maldives, which we were all delighted about despite the 12 hour flight and the 15 minute speed boat ride from the airport to the island of Male, where we stayed. Although the boat ride only took a short time it could be quite bumpy and although we wore lifejackets, some of us did not feel very safe. It was also quite difficult to step up from the boat to the quayside if the tide was low, in a pencil skirt with a heavy leather handbag. I was always pleased when the step up was not too high, especially as one of the crew had already fallen in completely clothed, bag and all.

Male itself was quite challenging as, like in many places, they have very strict rules which, of course, we had been advised we must adhere to.

During Ramadan, everything was closed throughout the day and it was extremely difficult to buy anything, even food, until after about 6 pm. Even the hotel pool was shut and when everything opened up the local people were served first as obviously they had been fasting all day. When going out for a walk, which I loved to walk into the quay and see the boats bringing in the huge tuna, we had to make sure we were covered up. The crew were warned about wearing very skimpy clothes and to keep our arms covered, failure to do this might result in the locals spitting at us as they felt it was an affront to their culture, so I made sure I always abided by the rules.

Although one day we were out walking when we turned the corner to see this angry mob coming towards us. My colleague and I decided to jump into a local shoe shop, of which there were many. It was a wonderful place to buy really lovely cheap shoes and we waited until things had quieten down but there is only just so long you can spend in a small shoe shop. Luckily all was quiet and we made our way to the shop I had found, where the materials were also beautiful and very cheap. They are excellent dressmakers and could copy any dress I took them and have it ready for me to collect the next day, it was very impressive.

If we were lucky, during the winter season there was often space available on the different nearby islands, so for a small sum, we could pay to take the boat from Male out to the island and stay in one of the beach villas, or water villas. I, of course, did not like the water villas, I was still always afraid I might come out of my villa and miss my step and end up in the water! I was more than happy to spend my rest days

162

lazing on the wonderful beaches reading my book and swimming in the beautiful clear blue water.

To my amazement, when we as a family stayed in the Maldives for my special birthday, I had been persuaded to go snorkeling. Yes, head under the water was a first for me and what had I got to lose? So with a lifejacket on, my family watched with much amusement as I put on the huge pair of flippers at the villa and then proceeded, with difficulty, to flip my way to the water. Of course, no one told me you put the flippers on at the water's edge!

The water was so warm and clear it was the most wonderful experience, but what I was not aware of was that every time I saw a shoal of beautifully coloured fish the excited shrieks of delight was coming up the snorkel tube for my family to hear, causing much amusement which they never let me forget. It was truly one destination, together with this snorkeling experience, that I had again ticked off my bucket list. Its true to say it is how I would imagine paradise to be.

CHAPTER 36

However, every day was not as perfect as this and just when everything was running smoothly, it had been decided by the Company to make some changes and start charging passengers for food and drink on board the shorthaul service. This decision did not go down at all well with some of the crew or the passengers and it made my decision easier in many ways to start thinking about leaving the job I had wanted for so long but was changing so much that it was becoming less and less enjoyable.

I had been considering handing in my notice but I was not sure what I would do as obviously I still needed to work, when my Manager called me into the office and wanted to discuss a new venture. He explained that he thought this would be the perfect opportunity for me and that I would be eligible to take on this new route and he was absolutely right, it was a marvellous opportunity.

The Company had decided to replace the old Concorde service with two new 318 aircrafts, 001 and 003, leaving from London City, one in the morning and one later in the day, to accommodate just 32 business people travelling to New York. The service would be a cross between First and Club World and because London City was so near Canary Wharf, passengers could be collected and brought to the airport, where just a short stroll to the gate across the tarmac they were ready to board.

The other advantage would be that due to the type of aircraft and how small it was, we would make a stop in Shannon in Ireland to refuel and clear customs. All the passengers, their hand luggage and crew had to leave the aircraft and go through the American immigration and customs. The staff were all Americans who had chosen to do a secondment for maybe up to five years and actually lived in the vicinity of Shannon. They all seemed to enjoy the job and it showed, as they were always so friendly and due to the fact that we were a small crew who travelled frequently on the service, we got to know them really well.

To the delight of the passengers, the above procedure meant that when we landed in New York, all they had to do was grab any luggage they may have checked in and land as domestic passengers before walking straight out to their waiting cars, or taxis. Just this alone made the service very popular, as there was always a long wait to clear immigration in New York and this procedure alone could take well over an hour if several flights had all landed at the same time.

The slight downside was that we would need to undertake SEP

training and this aircraft type would be added to the list of our yearly recurrent training. Luckily the 737 were being phased out so the 737 training would now be replaced with the 318 for some of us.

The two identical aircrafts were small but very impressive, with only 32 fully reclining seats, two seats on each side of the aircraft with all the latest On Air equipment so that business passengers could carry on working as if they were still in their offices. Some of them did just that and over the years I saw the same faces, it was nothing to see certain passengers flying out on Mondays on a regular basis and home again on our Tuesday night flight home. Passengers would comment that they saw more of us than their families in some cases.

It was important to welcome them on board by name, then apart from offering drinks and the meal service, I would know that they needed to be left alone to work. Attention to detail was extremely important, as this service was extremely expensive.

The onboard service was completely different from any other aircraft as, once again, the galleys were very small so most of the food and equipment was housed at the rear of the aircraft and had to be brought forward once we had taken off. It was extremely lucky that we operated the flight with only three crew, two crew at the back and one senior at the front. Once the trolleys were out and the service started there was not a lot of room to move around in the front galley, especially as there was a double crew seat and a toilet, which sometimes meant we would have queuing passengers to contend with as well.

There was a toilet at the rear, together with our two crew seats and although this galley was slightly bigger, it housed most of the equipment, trolleys and food which proved somewhat difficult to move through the cabin as being a small aircraft it could be quite bumpy. I remember one day we were at the rear of the aircraft with the trolley fully loaded, when the aircraft went through some turbulence and I landed on the lap of a very surprised passenger, together with the contents of some very expensive wine and champagne!

The training gave us explicit instructions on how this service would be carried out, as we had to serve an appetiser and choice of drinks on our way over to Shannon which took about one hour. Child's play once you have done a Jersey, plenty of time especially with only 32 passengers.

Once we had cleared Immigration and reboarded, the service would begin and I knew one of my greatest challenges was going to be the equipment. Luckily most passengers were well aware of how all the equipment worked, apart from the individual ipads which we handed out for inflight entertainment. It was either the ipad not working, or the earphones and this had to be sorted out as it was a big part of some passengers trip to watch the up-to-date movies.

Having sorted entertainment out, next would be lunch, then about an hour and a half before landing we would serve afternoon tea with scones, jam and cream - heaven, my favourite and I always hoped for refusals so there were some left and I was always put in charge of crew tea. Scone, cream next then jam, that is how I love them, but I am not that fussy, anyway will do. Special Carte D'Or cakes were also to die for.

With training completed, I was called into the office and told that I had been chosen to crew the inaugural flight home from New York to London City. The flight home was always direct, as there was no reason to stop on the way home and the flight time was about six and a half hours, whereas going out could take as long as eight hours, plus the one hour to Shannon added on.

As the three crew members were chosen, we were told to wear suitable attire, to be at Gatwick at a certain time where the car would take us to Heathrow to board the 777 New York flight as Club passengers. We would stay in the hotel overnight and then bring the flight home, which we were advised, would be carrying members of the press, so we should be careful of what we said.

All our uniform was to be spotless, no Target, or Bath and Body Works bags to be visible, must remember to take as little in my case as I could manage with on the trip, leaving enough space for shopping. Each crew member who operated this service was allocated a beautiful leather hat box and inside was the so called 'forage' cap, commonly called the 'Thunderbirds' hat. I loved it and still have it to this day sitting in its hat box in pristine condition.

Having to remember to pack all my uniform, including the leather handbag, which was rather large and rigid, took some packing. It was lucky that it was September and as the weather in New York was not that cold and I did not need to pack a warm coat and boots. I laid the entire uniform out on the bed and even went as far as my hair clips and scrunchie, I did not want to leave anything to chance.

I had already visited New York but I was so looking forward to being rostered this service on a regular basis, so that I could explore some of the sites. The first day, however, was spent going through the details of the service and listening to the outbound crew as to how everything had worked for them. As this would be a nightime service, we hoped some of the passengers may have already eaten in the beautiful Lounge in JFK, as this would give us a chance to see how it all actually functioned.

Although I was slightly anxious about this new aircraft and service, I am glad to say the flight crew, who we had also met at the hotel, were lovely and were always on this flight. Both the crew and passengers really loved these little aircrafts.

In normal circumstances, we would report to Gatwick fully dressed in our uniforms to make sure we had not forgotten anything, including hats, before being picked up by a small bus and taken to a hotel near London City to spend the night before flying out the next morning. It was a very long day from the early morning wake-up call to be ready for about 8 am, taken to LCY where we would check our luggage in and proceed through security to board the aircraft in readiness for boarding the passengers.

The early flight, having landed in Shannon to refuel and comply with US pre-clearance for everyone, would then fly to JFK and land around 2 pm American time, 7 pm in the UK. The journey to central Manhattan was always pretty busy, the volume of cars and the way everyone just seemed to switch lanes made the M25 look tame, so this journey would take anything up to an hour and beyond. I always knew I had arrived, as a little sleep on the bus was usually in order, by the constant hooting of the traffic for what seemed like very little reason, as it was usually pretty grid-locked with no one moving anywhere until the lights changed.

The arrival of this service was an absolute godsend, as it meant that my trips on the shorthaul flights were only kept to a minimum, just to keep my recency up for the protection of my licence, which was enough for me. Although my yearly SEP training was becoming a lot more complex with the removal of the 737s came the introduction of the Airbus 318, 319, 320 and 321, one variant of which we did not even work on which proved extremely difficult when it came to the exam.

We stayed, firstly, at the Concorde Hotel which was very near to Bloomingdales. This was an amazing shop and I was always being asked to buy the Little Brown Bag, which is just a very simple caramel brown coloured plastic range of bags, bearing the above logo, very famously related to this beautiful shop and loved by all, especially visitors to America.

The Concorde Hotel was also very near to Tiffanys, which is another wonderful store, even if there never seems to be any visible prices. Very often we would meet up in Central Park and go for breakfast near the Boating Lake and visit the zoo on the way back. We also went to visit the Guggenheim Museum which was right at the far end of Central Park, quite a long walk but well worth a visit.

We seemed to be forever moving hotels whilst operating this service, as the Concorde hotel was eventually sold, but one of the best moves was the Fitzpatrick Hotel on Lexington Ave, which was right opposite Grand Central Station and even better two doors along from Bath and

Body Works, what a result! This was wonderful news to the crew as we would arrive from the flight and still be in time, even on the later flight, to manage a shopping trip before they closed at 9 pm. If we did miss them, they opened again at 8 am so an early morning trip before breakfast was on the cards and, of course, we did not have to carry the bags too far.

Sadly, although the hotel was very central, we ended up being moved again, two or three times at least and ended up behind Macys, which was central on 34th but extremely busy. However, I was able to walk to my favourite park, Bryant Park, where I used to go to Panera, located just around the corner and buy my breakfast or lunch and go and sit and people watch.

The heat in the summer was almost unbearable in New York, the heat seemed to burn out of the buildings and it was hard to get out much after the shops opened at 10 am. Likewise, in the winter it was absolutely freezing and even in our winter uniform coats, pashminas and gloves, the cold almost took your breath away. It was like the two extremes, my case would have to hold a really substantial winter coat, hat, earmuffs, scarf, gloves, thermals and very warm boots. In fact, everything I could think of to protect me from the cold. It was like being in the arctic.

I would dread my nose running as getting a tissue out was not an option, as I never removed my gloves and if I left the liquid it would just freeze to my face, not a pretty sight.

Having so many clothes on was very uncomfortable when entering the shops, as it was like the sublime to the ridiculous, it was so hot I nearly passed out with the heat and had to unwrap some of my layers, which would need to be replaced again when going back outside. Although the snow was really lovely and the parks looked like a winter wonderland and very picturesque, however, the underground pavement heating in New York meant the streets were passable although the deep snow became piled up on the sidewalks in great drifts.

It was not unusual for heavy snow to fall, delaying our departure enforcing our having to stay in New York until the runway was cleared and made safe for aircraft to take off. Likewise, if heavy snow started to fall on our arrival at JFK, the aircraft would need to be de-iced before we left the stand but the traffic out on the runway was always very congested and by the time we had been in the queue for take-off, the de-icing would have to be carried out all over again. This could result in us having to return to the hotel and wait until the snow cleared.

My family were always very jealous of the amount of snow I had been lucky enough to experience, as we seldom have snow in the UK now and when we do it usually is not enough to build even a small snowman as it melts so quickly, its been a long time since we have had a really large amount of deep snow.

We also had the experience of being marooned in New York due to the Ash Cloud in 2010. It was fortunate that we had plenty of shops to go and buy more clothes and plenty of places to visit, but not so lucky if, as some crew were, stuck somewhere that did not have any facilities. There was also the big question of childcare to think about with those crew who relied on family and nurseries, as we had no idea when we would be able to fly home.

Sadly in 2016, it was decided that as Shannon airport shut at 2pm it was not cost effective to pay staff, including Immigration officials until 4 pm when our second aircraft landed. It was therefore decided to cancel this second service, much to the annoyance of passengers who could spend a day in the office, then leave at the last minute to travel to London City in the afternoon and arrive in New York that evening in time to go to a business dinner, or meeting. So this cut the service to one flight a day, excluding Saturdays.

The loss of this second flight caused great sadness amongst the crew, as everyone so enjoyed these trips and obviously we would still be rostered them but unfortunately not as many.

CHAPTER 37

I know I am not very good with change but my Son, Max, had moved out to live in a flat and I was left with the big decision if I would have to sell the house, much to everyone's dismay, as the family desperately wanted me to keep it. However, I was getting older and I was not actually paying anything off the actual mortgage and I knew I had to shift this debt whilst I was working, otherwise, I would have this decision to make when I eventually retired.

Reluctantly, I had to put the house on the market but I knew it was going to be such a big wrench, especially as I had managed to do one or two improvements, like having the windows replaced to stop the howling draught and seeing the sky through the cracks in the woodwork. Showing people around my beloved house and listening to disparaging comments like 'You only have one bathroom' and 'Oh, No Garage'. I desperately wanted to say 'Surprisingly it does not have either on the sales particulars, so what do you expect' but these might be prospective purchasers, so I resisted the temptation.

In truth, I did not want anyone to buy my house that I had fought to keep for so long, despite all odds, but I would have to get used to looking for another property for myself. JP came with me but with the small amount of money I would have left from my sale, plus a mortgage that I had worked so hard to procure, by making sure I had a good credit score, had taken some doing.

We were looking around a small bungalow when from quite out of the blue JP suddenly said 'You know you could just take a leap of faith, I could sell my property buy into your house, and there would be no need to move'. I could not get my head around this at first, as we were standing in this empty new-build house, this was a wonderful suggestion but was I ready to take this huge step?

I was my own boss, was I ready to share my life and my home with someone again on a permanent basis, as it worked so well that I had my house and JP had his, so in a way, we always had a bolthole to go to. There was always this huge question that I could not seem to come to terms with and that was trust and I knew only too well the pitfalls that could happen once we actually lived together. Questions ran through my head, like supposing it all went wrong, I would still have to sell up, I had made so many wrong decisions in my life.

Elizabeth, Max and Alex all got on pretty well with JP and I had discussed all the options with them and they thought I should take up JP's offer and keep the house. I suppose a beach hut could be an alternative, although even they sell for about £30,000 or more.

Did I want to be on my own for the rest of my life? JP knew what my flying life was like, in respect of how long I was away, which would give him time on his own and he enjoyed coming with me on the longer trips, so maybe it could work.

It was an extremely difficult decision but let's just say I put my life into stages, I have experienced many ups and downs but on this occasion, I made the right decision. I moved into the next stage of my life and JP moved into his, which was a loft extension solely for his use as a man cave/music room, which he completely designed, I do not even clean up there.

We had been out to Hong Kong several times and Elizabeth and Max had always wanted to come, so it was lovely to be able to take them with us. They experienced what it was like to travel in Club Class seats and actually see just what my job entailed, I really enjoyed watching them laying back in their seats watching the up-to-date films, eating nice food and enjoying the high life.

The whole trip was wonderful, especially for JP as this was home for him and he spoke Cantonese which made things so much easier for us. Elizabeth and Max met up with old school friends who they had kept in contact with and one of them just happened to be the Manager at the hotel where we were staying. We were upgraded immediately to a beautiful suite overlooking the bay which was spectacular, watching the cruise liners docking and then setting sail in the evenings.

So many wonderful places to visit and even just crossing from Kowloon to the mainland of Hong Kong on the Star Ferry was an experience, before going on the tram up to the Peak where the view was breathtaking, especially at night. In fact, the views at night were fantastic from both sides but especially walking along the promenade on the Kowloon side and looking across to Hong Kong where all the buildings were lit up and constantly changing colours was an amazing sight.

Everyone wanted to go to Ocean Park to visit the Pandas and we were not disappointed. On cue, these beautiful animals all came out and sat right in front of us chewing on their bamboo and completely oblivious to all the attention they were receiving from all the visitors.

It was then time to take the overhead cable car to the park itself where they all went on some of the largest rides I had ever seen and I was quite happy just looking on. I only had to look at some of the people who had just come off the rides to know that it was not for me but JP, Elizabeth and Max just loved it as they screamed their way upside down on some of the rides. I was in charge of knowing where they were sitting in order to take their photos on the way past me, although very often by the time I realised it was them I was too late, as they shot by at such speed and had to wait until next time around. They were more than happy to queue and go on the rides again and were still on the water ride when the park was starting to close.

I just enjoyed watching them all having such a wonderful time, they really deserved this and it was a very special time as I knew this would probably be the last time that just the four of us would be together and I was going to make the most of this trip. We were all moving on with our lives, Elizabeth, Max and Alex all had partners, good jobs and were happy, what more could a Mother wish for - well maybe one small wish in time!

On the way home, having been served their dinner and then all tucked up in their Club Class bed, they began to realise how tiring it was for crew to be working most of the night and then having to drive home at the end of the trip. 'We do not know how you do it'. Mind you neither did I sometimes on a very busy flight.

I was beginning to realise that full-time flying, together with the long drive home was getting more and more tiring and as I was in a better position now financially, it was decided I would drop down to a 75% contract, which would mean flying three weeks a month. Having a week off every month was wonderful and as I was becoming more and more aware that my parents were now becoming quite elderly and it would mean I could spend time helping them instead of rushing to see them on my way home, or on one of my two days off.

I managed to work out the roster system as the company was becoming more and more technical and it seemed everything had to be done on the computer, which I and many crew did not like. However, I was still able to get myself on the JFK flights at least two or three times a month so I must have been doing something right, with a bit of shorthaul thrown in for good measure.

Yes, shorthaul, well this type of flying had never been my favorite as I think longhaul was in my blood and of course what I was used to. I still enjoyed greeting the passengers on arrival at the aircraft but when you have done this on three or four flights there and back in a day and said goodbye to about 130 on each flight, even my smile was waning.

It was challenging at times when trying to serve all the passengers on a shorthaul if the flight time was short. Some passengers would drink the bar dry and leave nothing for the passengers who had not been served at the rear. So we would try and have two trolleys, one at the front with two of us and one crew member bringing up a trolley from the rear. This was alright until we needed more hot water and the crew member had to take his or her trolley back, as trolleys could not be left alone in the aisles, to replenish our stocks.

There was also the problem of the handing out of the food, ie.

sandwiches. Either everyone wanted the same fillings, or wanted the vegetarian option, leaving nothing for the real vegetarians, it was almost impossible to please everyone and after all its only a sandwich. On occassions I had opened sandwiches but only for it to be flung back at me which if I ducked went all over the other passengers!

To make matters worse it was decided the Company would start charging for all the food and drink served on board to come in line with what other airlines had been doing for some time. Some of the crew relished this idea as they had maybe worked for other airlines and were used this procedure and liked the fact we would get commission on all the sales. I, like many of our colleagues, knew this was how future flying was going but knew customer service was going to suffer, especially on shorter flights where speed was of the essence.

On certain flights, if passenger loads allowed, there would be two crew at the front. Please let it be me as this would be a Club non-paying service and three crew at the back where they would operate a paying service. Where only three crew, or maybe four crew were allocated to a flight the Senior would have to manage up the front on his or her own, whilst the other two or three would manage the rear of the aircraft.

A well known Company, who knew nothing about aircraft food, was given the task of supplying the whole of the shorthaul fleet with a small selection of food and drink as per the menu in the front seat pocket and only credit card would be accepted, no cash.

There is a huge difference between a store in a town or village, with a huge backup warehouse attached whereby when shelves start to empty, if correctly managed, can be replenished by further supplies. We were travelling in an aircraft which had been loaded with what was thought to be enough food and drink for the whole aircraft, but seldom was, with no backup whatsoever. I wanted to throw myself off the aircraft into the sea with the sheer frustration of it all, as it was so difficult to cater for everyone's needs, whilst still giving good customer service with a smile.

By the time I had reached the first six rows we had already sold out of some of the items on the menu, so I was dreading how the rest of the aircraft would be. Trying to keep everything calm, we decided one of us would serve the passengers whilst the other took the money and the crew member at the rear would run backwards and forwards heating the hot food, whilst being aware we still had so many passengers to serve before we prepared for landing.

The trolley is very visible to all the passengers so you would think having made a loudspeaker announcement that the menu for the food was in their front pocket and everyone would know what they wanted when I reached their row, but no. "What do you have?" was more than often asked. I would reply "Tea, Coffee including Cappuccino and Latte, and Hot Chocolate." "Do you have Expresso?," "No" (because it is not on the list) "Do you have any Milkshakes?," and so it went on.

Then the people who see the trolley and you ask them what you can get them and then turn to the family and start a long discussion about what they would like. It was so frustrating and not more so than for the passengers at the back who were just waiting to be served.

When an order was placed, no tray tables had been pulled down and even worse I would hand the passenger their drink and they would then lose the use of their arms. "Would you please pull down your tray table" and even then the person in the window would expect the person sitting next to them to hand them their drink or I would have to stretch over all the passengers to reach them. It's as if they had all lost the use of their arms!

I would try to explain that we did not have a backup wagon floating behind us as what is loaded onboard the aircraft is all we have. The desperation I felt when the Percy Pigs and Friends were getting low as a passenger spat at me saying "How can you sleep at night, I have four children and I want four packets of Percy Pigs." I explained I sleep very well thank you for asking and as I only have two packets of Percy Pigs perhaps they could share and have two packets of something else, maybe crisps to go with them. I so wanted to say there are some children who are not fortunate enough to ever have one sweet, let alone a whole packet. I advised that he could have bought these same sweets in the Terminal before boarding and might I suggest he does that next time to avoid disappointment. Time for me to move the trolley on to the next passenger.

The rows over the food caused many delays and at times some passengers did not receive their drinks and food until it was virtually time to secure in and land, which was in many instances due to all the above and passengers selfishness. The longer shorthaul flights gave us a lot more time to deal with all these problems.

I knew I was turning into Victor Meldrew and I always promised myself I would know when the time was right for me to hang up my wings and I suddenly felt this could be coming very soon.

CHAPTER 38

At least in the midst of the shorthaul I was so lucky to still have some longhaul flights, which included the JFK, so I could not really complain.

We had once again moved, this time to the Lexington Hotel, still only a couple of blocks away from Bath and Body Works, which was a good move from the point of view of carrying heavy bags of their delicious candles back. These and the handsoaps were the two items most of my family and friends wanted me to bring back. Over the years I cannot imagine how much I had managed to pack in my luggage, I only know the girls in the store greeted me by name and I knew all of them by name and all about their families and knitted for their babies when they became pregnant.

I arrived on this particular day at the Lexington and our rooms were not quite ready as the earlier crew had been late in checking out due to a delay, which very often happened. The Manager said if we were free the next day would we like to go and see the apartment where Marilyn Monroe and Joe DiMaggio had lived for about two years when they married in the fifties, named the Norma Jeane Suite, as the guests who were staying overnight would have left on an early flight.

The apartment was amazing and although it had been updated it had been done so tastefully in the Art Deco black and white design of the 50s, and a dash of red synonymus with Marilyn herself, so as not to lose its original style. There was a Lounge with a stunning bar and kitchen to one side, a bathroom, beautiful furnishings in the bedroom and best of all the most wonderful views from the huge 200ft balcony. We just had to have our photo taken on such an iconic balcony, where Marilyn had been photographed many times, for our scrapbook!

Having had a taste of the Marilyn Monroe era, we decided we would go and visit the famous pavement where the film The Seven Year Itch was shot so we could see if our skirts had the same affect of blowing up with the blast from the subway. Alas, even though we wore our best knickers, our skirts never moved and all we heard was the noise of the subway that was running underneath, very disappointing but perhaps lucky for the passersby to be spared such a sight!

I had some wonderful trips whilst doing this JFK route and I was never tired of the actual flight itself which, although very precise, was a pleasure to crew and as there were so few of us on this route, we used to often fly with the same crew members which was also a nice change.

One Christmas I remember one of the crew arranged a trip to Radio

City in New York to see the Christmas Spectacular show in 3D which was absolutely beautiful. Sometimes we would arrange to meet and go shopping over in New Jersey as we had managed to negotiate how to use the subways. It seemed extremely difficult at first to work out which way to go, either Uptown or Downtown. However, like being in London, once I had gone the wrong way once or twice, I soon got the hang of it.

Just like our underground, I had some strange encounters whilst using the subway. At Christmas groups of people would get on the train and move through the carriages singing carols to raise money for charity, not sure what charity but it was very festive. One of the scariest moments on the subway was I had been standing up on the train as it was quite busy, when a passenger moved and I sat down and trust me I sat next to a black man who had a huge rucksack.

I had not really taken any notice when I sat down but suddenly a passenger got on at the next stop, whereupon the man sitting next to me jumped up and hit him with his rucksack and said he was going to knife him as he did not like the colour of his skin. A big fracas started between them and I felt so sorry for this unassuming man who had just merely stepped on the train minding his own business. The strangest thing was he was swearing all sorts of abuse at this poor man saying he was only looking at him because he was black, the other man was black too.

I was very scared as he started to reach in his bag and I, like the other passengers on the train, started moving and getting off the train. When the train came into the station, whether or not it was the station I needed, I was, like others, getting off. Unfortunately, as I got off the train the man who had been doing all the shouting got off as well, so it was like some farce, so we waited then just as the doors closed we all jumped back on the train again, together with the poor unsuspecting man.

He was visibly shaken, a really lovely man, I felt so sorry for him and as we talked to him to see if there was anything we could do for him. He explained, he too could not understand why he had picked on him but we were all glad that he did not have a knife or a gun, as at one stage we were not too sure.

I loved the excitement that always surrounded New York, there was always something going on. Very often filming was taking place either near Grand Central or in Central Park, especially when the ice skating rink was open as it was a magical setting for a lot of films. I would often stand and watch the filming hoping to see someone famous which was often the case but I nearly ended up in hospital during one of these encounters.

I had been to the Dollar shop as it was soon to be Halloween, so my hands were pretty full when I looked across at Grand Central. On the sidewalk there was, as I thought, my all time favourite actor, Denzil Washington. I was so busy watching him that I missed my footing and the next thing I knew I had hit the pavement with such force that I thought I had broken my wrist and had damaged the face on my watch. As I was being helped up I could see my jeans were torn and there was blood seeping through the gap.

It was lunchtime rush hour and everyone had gathered around, one person offered to call an ambulance but all I wanted to do was stand up and pretend I was perfectly alright. Another passerby was picking up my witches masks and broomsticks, another was rescuing some other Halloween goodies that were scattered all over the sidewalk. I was just hoping that it was not Denzil who was filming, as otherwise I would have been mortified for him to have seen me in this state. As for going to the Hospital, I could just see myself explaining to the Airline Company just why I could not work the flight home.

Everyone had been very kind but I just wanted the ground to open up and swallow me in as my Halloween merchandise had been repacked for me. All I wanted to do was confirm that I was absolutely fine so I could hobble back to my hotel and repair the damage. Luckily after a soak in the bath, the scrazes on my knees looked worse than they were and once the blood had been wiped away my knee was swollen but the cuts were not deep. I would hopefully be able to hide the damage with my nearly black stockings. Worst of all, however, I never did ever get to see Denzil!

I decided it was time for me to go part-time, which meant two weeks on and two weeks off. This enabled me to keep an eye on my elderly mother, as sadly my lovely dad had passed away after a really short illness. He had prostate cancer and I think he had known for sometime that at 92 he was not going to live very much longer. Luckily, he went into hospital and three weeks later he died, so I was relieved that he did not suffer for very long and on the morning of the day he died I was able to tell him that I was going to be a grandma and he a great-grandad, as Elizabeth was expecting a baby boy.

Sadly he never met his grandson but they do say as one life ends another begins and I do believe this as although he has never met his great-grandad, he talks about him often and recently raised money in a sponsored Race for Life event in his memory. My dad would have been so proud of him.

My parents had been married for over 65 years and my mother found it difficult to manage as my dad looked after everything financially. Dad believed he went out to work and supplied the money, whilst my mother brought up us four children. This proved very difficult as she had never paid any bills or put a card in a cash machine. When I took her shopping, my dad always left the money beside the clock for housekeeping as he had done throughout their marriage.

This may have worked in past years but now in her late 80s, was going to prove extremely difficult, as trying to teach dad how to use a mobile phone was useless, let alone get my mother to use one. I remember receiving a call from my dad's mobile phone and it was from a complete stranger to whom he had just handed the phone to and asked to ring me. He had broken down and luckily having hailed down a passing motorist, he had picked one that was kind enough to make the call for him so that I could arrange for the AA to go out to assist him. Yes, he had been a member with the AA all that longtime since joining them when I was a child and still had the original AA badge.

I only allowed my dad to drive around locally as it was safer for all the other road users in his area. He had been driving since the war years, never taken a test and when I applied for a blue badge for him to enable him to park in the disabled bay, he thought this included the space outside the local pub that was meant for him alone, so he informed the local constabulary! As luck would have it he never knew he had been asked to go for a driving test after he reversed into the local Police car several times whilst parking in 'his space' as he died shortly before the test date.

The writing was on the cards with my mother on her own and the whole face of flying completely changing, maybe it was time to ease down with a view to retiring as I had managed to achieve what I wanted. My brother was running his own business in another part of the country and my sister Barbara was still working and I knew my mother did not like the fact that I was away so much. The annual SEP recurrent training seemed to come around very quickly and despite having done it so many times, it never got any easier but I was always pleased to say that over the years I always managed to pass. However, I wanted to leave on a high, after all this time I would have been mortified to fail and have to retake the test.

I had never been in the right place at the right time but for once it worked out for me. I had been wanting to spend much more time with my wonderful grandson who was growing up fast and I did not want to drive to the airport through another Winter. So I already had it in my mind that I would stay for another three months before handing in my notice. However, my mother had a fall and when I returned home from a trip, her neighbour rang me to say that she had not seen my mother and her newspaper was sticking out of the door still.

I tried to raise her by telephone without success, so I got back in my car and drove the 35 minutes to her home where I found her unconscious on the kitchen floor. She had taken off her Lifeline to get undressed and had gone into the kitchen for some water but fell and had laid there all night.

Her pulse was extremely shallow, she was barely breathing and extremely cold as she was undressing ready to go to bed so had very few clothes on. I grabbed some blankets whilst ringing the Ambulance and whilst I was doing this she stopped breathing. All my training came back to me but I was shaking as it is extremely hard to concentrate on a real body as I was only used to a dummy. Whilst talking to the operator, I started CPR. I never felt so grateful when I heard the siren of the ambulance arriving at the door. I let them take over.

My mother survived but never really forgave me as she wanted to die and be with our dad.

CHAPTER 39

Just as I was about to hand in my notice I became aware that the Company was looking to reduce the number of crew with older Contracts by offering them a package. The deal was that if we accepted the money, we had to stay on and to carry out the flying programme for the Summer and leave in October. So I agreed and instead of leaving in March I took the money and left in October having been with the Company for 22 years. I was also allowed to keep my concessions for the 22 years of two flights a year, if space was available on my selected choice of flight.

Handing in my prestigious uniform and pass was extremely hard, although I was allowed to keep my special hat in its hatbox by way of concession.

Little did I know at the time that the following year would be one of the most disastrous years for many of my friends and colleagues in the airline industry with the arrival of this terrible Covid virus. We just have to hope that with the vaccine, people will start to travel again.

I wrote this novel during the long hours of the Covid lockdown and I would like to dedicate this book to the millions of people around the world who have lost love ones like myself. We lost our mother aged 95 on the 2nd January 2021 to Covid, likewise my dear old school friend who also lost her Mother a week after also aged 95.

I am so grateful that my family and friends have received the vaccine, which is the glimmer of light at last at the end of a very long tunnel. We will not be beaten by this virus or anything else that comes our way and will survive to remember all those who have not been so fortunate.

This book shows the journey from birth to adulthood and how an Essex, Convent girl called Sharon, worked her way through all the trials and tribulations that life threw her way to reach her goals. After all, as William Shakespeare's phrase from As you Like It begins with "All the World's a Stage" and mine has definitely been just that. However hard life gets, whatever age and background you come from, remember, anything and everything is possible. When I look and hear of the adversities some people have been through, I consider myself to have been extremely lucky.

I still find myself looking up in the sky when I am in my garden and seeing an aircraft and thinking what would I be doing at this point of the flight. If I go on board as a passenger when the call is made to put the doors into Manual or Automatic and cross check, I still think I should be doing something and not just sitting there as a passenger looking forward to my holiday.

My job as cabin crew has allowed me to fly all over the world, staying in some very luxurious hotels that I could have never afforded. I have seen some wonderful places and met some amazing people and maybe you were one of them. If you were, I so hoped you enjoyed your flight as much as I did. I met Royalty and many lovely celebrities, although disappointingly not Denzil Washington, but there is still time and hopefully I will be standing up next time!

Please take me with you when you next fly and spare a thought for the crew who, hopefully from this book I have made you realise, are not just 'chicken or beef' served by trolley dollies. They are working hard, looking after your safety and making your flight a wonderful start to your holiday, something I always tried to do, so that I could hear you say "That was a wonderful flight, we really enjoyed it, the crew were so lovely, thank you" as we said our goodbyes.

• • •

Lightning Source UK Ltd.
Milton Keynes UK
UKHW021834081221
395328UK00003B/44